THE MAPLE LEAF FOR QUITE A WHILE

THE MAPLE LEAF
FOR QUITE A WHILE

HEATHER GILEAD

With 4 pages of photographs

LONDON
J. M. DENT & SONS LTD

ILLUSTRATIONS

MY FATHER must have been going on for eighty when he pronounced upon his marriage. The communication was made to Vera, an intimate friend of my sister Lottie. He had met Vera in the main street of Regalia, shortly after her own marriage, and stopped to congratulate her. She had, as she told Lottie after, been touched by his warmth and sincerity as well as his optimism. He had known her of course since she was a little girl in pigtails coming to spend a night or a week-end with his own little girls in pigtails, and had followed her career from those far-off days of games and gigglings through school, normal school and the years of school-teaching that had gone on and on and on, long after most of her contemporaries had left their jobs to marry and make homes. My father had never met the groom, and was not much of a collector of gossip, so he would not know that Vera was stuck with the oft warmed-over remains of a hundred near-matrimonial escapades.

So he shook her hand warmly and told her how glad he was that she was married. He was *for* marriage. He was the sort of man who could say this unequivocally and without embarrassment.

He hoped that Vera and Fred would be happy. He hoped that they would be as happy as he and his wife had been. He was emphatic about this married happiness enjoyed by my mother and him. He figured out in his slow way how many years that happiness had been going on, and as he had grown-up grand-children at the time his pronouncement could scarcely be immature or ill-considered. He would have spoken without irony. He would have stated his facts and sentiments plainly, as he saw them, and his eloquence and vocabulary were adequate to all normal occasions.

Vera, as I understand it, was a little curious. She doubted neither his honesty nor his goodwill, but she had been alive something like forty years without discerning any great numbers of perpetual honeymoons. I don't suppose she suspected my parents' marriage of being any worse than the average, but this hint of protracted prairie idyll surprised her so much that she asked Lottie about it.

Lottie was surprised too. I don't suppose that she had given any thought as to whether our parents' marriage was good, bad or indifferent. Marriage in their generation simply *was*. Once contracted it had to be allowed to run its course, like mumps or diphtheria, and there wasn't much use inventing a lot of categories and classifications. Lottie didn't see our parents' marriage as a tragedy or a cosmic error or anything like that. But that anyone so intimately involved as my father—if the word 'intimate' can be used in conjunction with my father—should go out of his way to dwell upon its happiness, and should accuse our mother of being happy in it too, all those years . . .

If Lottie was surprised, I was flabbergasted when I heard about it. I was youngest; except for a boy who died in infancy and whom I cannot even remember, although the effort to do so evokes a dim recollection of my mother weeping quietly about the house without interrupting her work, and everlastings— popular funerary flowers—dried and gathering dust about the house for a long time. But home was a cheerful enough place as I first recall it. There was a lot of life around: my three sisters, two brothers, hired men, sometimes a hired girl, old Morgan who lived with us. As the girls grew up there were assorted boy friends and girl friends coming for week-ends. There were sing-songs around the piano; 'swimming', which consisted of wading and splashing about in one of the less muddy little lakes until being routed by mosquitoes; tobogganing parties in winter. My sisters got on rather well together. They were twelve, ten and eight years older than I. Then there were my two brothers, four and five years older than I. But all too soon my sisters were away at school, then married or working. The boys were early engaged in men's work, as farm boys used to be. I might almost have been an only child about the house then.

And so, by the time I was eight or ten, the house was too quiet, too free of distraction, for me to remain unaware of my mother's chronic unhappiness which she had converted into specific grievances.

I don't mean that her grievances were imaginary. To name only a few, the ineradicable bed-bugs and bats infesting the house were all too real. The winter cold, which sometimes obliged her to make a tent of blankets over her precious house plants and put hot rocks inside so that they wouldn't freeze overnight in the warmest room in the house, was real enough, as was the way that same house could hold the summer heat so that sleep was impossible hours after a teeth-chattering chill had settled out of doors. There was the impossibility of keeping milk and meat fresh during the hot summer—I recommend a few meals off tainted meat to anyone who thinks refrigeration a luxury in North America. And there was water, of course—or rather the scarcity of water. During the long years of drought, when all the shallow wells dried up, water was a constant tribulation. It had to be pumped by hand from a deep well—our nearest one was two miles away—and carried home in tanks and cans on horse-drawn wagons. The men hated it: it was a whole day's dreary hard labour for two men to fill the tank. As for the housekeeper, she washed mountains of dishes and greasy pots in a little pan of water that became soupier and soupier. Even worse was the cream separator and all those milk pails; milk vessels are curiously nasty to clean even when water is abundant. We budgeted water like money—and not just for a few weeks at the end of the summer, but for years on end. The water we washed our hair in was saved and reheated for baths and, if not too filthy, would be used again to scrub floors. Clothes had no hope of ever being whiter-than-white. We bathed weekly in a little basin. The men, encrusted with a week's grime from the fields, rated full basins, but children did not. Every chore was harder and, being done, was less well done for want of water. No house-keeper who has experienced a prolonged, acute shortage would swap an abundance of water for all the gadgets and mechanical aids imaginable.

In short, my mother's legitimate grievances were legion, which is probably why it took me years to realize that they were only incidental to the incantation she had manufactured out of a selection from them.

The problem was not our old friend sex. I shared my parents' bedroom until I was quite old—four, or maybe even five. I heard them. The puzzle was not so much what they were doing, but how they could be so untypically amicable there in the dark.

3

They were friendly, affectionate—cheerful even. But, come the dawn, and nothing much remained but recriminations on the one side and, on the other, the door quietly, definitively closing. No sooner had he gone out, shutting the door behind him, than my mother would start muttering to herself as she worked, rehearsing the next grievance to be aired so that no time need be lost in delivery when my father should appear in the doorway again.

By the time I was the sensitive age of thirteen or so this nagging, although seldom directed towards me, had become a sort of Chinese water torture. I assumed that it must be just as bad, or worse even, for my poor father.

As he closed the door on it one day I rounded on her—it must have been shocking, like being savaged by a bunny rabbit—and announced, 'If ever I speak to my husband like that I hope he beats me!' Then I stood awaiting the wrath to come. She turned her back. I thought at first that she hadn't heard, and wondered if I should ever get enough courage screwed up to speak out again. She resumed her work about the kitchen. After a few minutes I realized that she was silently weeping. I crept off, appalled. I doubt if she had wept since the death of that infant son so many years before.

I dare say my mother forgot that incident years ago, but I cannot remember it even now without my very bowels cringing in protest. Suddenly I knew that she had not been born a nag, that it was too late to change anything at all, and that consequently I had exposed her to herself in this cruel fashion to no purpose whatsoever. I never attempted to enter into that one-sided quarrel again, although it was now more intolerable than ever. My eagerness to get away from that house showed through sometimes, although I tried hard to suppress all evidence of it. She would pounce on all such manifestations and worry them with the oblique and apparently irrelevant irritation with which she clothed all her anguish.

Seal bats' ears with wax, release them in a space fraught with obstacles around which they have been accustomed to navigate without difficulty, and they will promptly clobber themselves on every obstacle in sight and be reduced to squeaking, quivering disorientation. Marriage must have been something like that for my mother, except that instead of being released into the midst

4

of obstacles she was, so to speak, released into the midst of infinity, so that none of her emitted signals were ever bounced back to her. And this was just where the constantly reiterated folklore of romantic sexual love promised the perfect resonator, the great adventure into genuine intimacy.

Previously she had lived in Iowa, and taught school for years in a pre-industrial society which held the teaching profession in great respect. She had in addition been accustomed to living in a numerous family in which she was the eldest daughter. And almost on the doorstep of the family farm was the little town in which she taught and wherein were numerous cousins, churches filled with weddings, socials, good works, gigglings of girls, and all. She could have spent few hours of real solitude, and those few would probably have been well furnished with expectation as to the next meeting. It was a life to which her extrovert nature would have been perfectly attuned: useful, busy, unpretentious, with probably a good deal of pre-Freudian horse-and-buggy gaiety. In this life she would hardly have apprehended herself and the meaning of her existence except as it was reflected back from the lives about her. Her mind had no talent for abstract or general thought. She would not even have seen herself as *a* teacher, but as *the* teacher of Polly and Alvin and a whole string of all-too-concrete little specimens. Having little imagination, she would not have imagined herself without an adequate supply of perpetual, direct human relationships.

And so of course she married the most utterly self-sufficient man I have ever known. He was about forty before he married. He had known and had indeed been engaged to my mother for some years, but some illness in her family had necessitated her presence in Iowa. Most men would have felt the inconvenience of bachelorhood in a pioneer country (as central Alberta was then) without servants, shops, laundries or even any way of banking fires for long periods during the arctic winters, but it seems unlikely that the inconvenience of single life made much more impression on my father than the subsequent convenience of matrimony. He ate all the food set before him, good, bad or indifferent, with the same grateful gusto. A scrubbed, tidy, be-doileyed and needleworked house or a pigsty, it was all one to him. He blamed so little that his praise held small merit.

5

Although he was true to the friends of his youth, and corresponded faithfully over half a century with some of them (do any of the men of my generation do the same?), his real intimates were books. He read and read and re-read Mark Twain, newspapers, Ralph Connor, Edgar Wallace, Jack London, Robert Service, Zane Grey, seed catalogues—anything and everything. I always found him kindly and courteous, loving after his absent-minded fashion, and having been accustomed to him from the beginning of my life his seemed a perfectly comfortable and satisfactory sort of love to me. He had no vices other than reading, wasted neither his time nor modest means on tobacco, drink, cards or women. But he did not really need our attention or suffer any compulsion to make us need him.

Characteristically, my mother's reading was almost confined (except for her old home-town newspaper) to social reading— to reading aloud to us during the long winter evenings, when we were children. As I remember, she read rather well, so well that one would have thought she must enjoy it enough to read for her own sake as well as ours. But she almost never picked up a book unless to share it. And of course she would have been married years already before there were any children old enough to be up and require entertainment and instruction after supper.

She must have come to Canada in the frozen February of 1911 with the cheerful certainty that her companionship would be food and drink to a desperately deprived lonely man. She had brought with her the parlour games she loved to play: checkers, chinese checkers, carroms, croquinole. She must have had visions of long winter evenings bright with talk and games and laughter. She got the long evenings all right, but filled with pages being turned in silence, except for the occasional burst of unexplained chuckling. There were no respectful school children now, no women's talk, no neighbours, no social events—not even any strangers, not even a view of a road down which something moves. Just silence, except for the implacable intimacy of the bulky iron cooking stove, the splintery rough board floors, cooking, dirty dishes, the washboard and mending. It must have left her as bruised and baffled—and as shrilly resentful—as the sealed-up bats.

How many years it took her to become a sort of broken record,

6

reiterating a catalogue of peripheral grievances, I don't know. That marriage had endured twenty years before I became aware of it and decided to be bruised by my poor father's martyrdom.

Martyrdom! This quiet, courteous, tranquil little man was not one to excite outrage. Besides, by the time I learned that his serenity was not a brave and stoic performance, but the Real McCoy, he was long since in his quiet prairie graveyard. No, not outrage; I didn't feel outrage. But that he should have lived with that woman all those years and never even noticed her pain! And he was a kindly, generous man—it would have grieved him, I'm sure, had any measure of it registered. . . .

It's a wonder there is so little genuine domestic mayhem, really.

IT WAS NOT until I tried to make some scant record of my parents, of the worlds they came from, created, lived in— and outlived—that I realized how mistaken one is to equate familiarity with knowledge. And a good part of the little I *do* think I know about them is certainly inaccurate, being only half understood by the child that I was when I apprehended it.

My mother is descended on her father's side from a Hessian mercenary hired out to George III during the American War of Independence. At the end of that war he sensibly deserted the English army to accept the American offer of amnesty, free land and citizenship. During the late nineteen-forties one of his descendants, still resident in the Carolinas where he had originally settled, traced as many descendants as possible and invited them to a gathering of the clan. More than a hundred turned up—heaven knows how many hundreds they represented —from all parts of the continent. It is not unlikely that many of them were teetotal.

On the maternal side, my mother boasted an ancestor called John Ireland. The typhus-ravaged immigrant ship from which he had been taken, an orphaned baby-in-arms, had been largely filled with Irish; so they named him Ireland.

Of my father's antecedents I know even less. His surname was English—or anglicized. My mother did not exactly approve of her father-in-law, but none of us would necessarily have thought the less of him for that. He was the only grandparent who survived long enough to be known to any of us. He was dead before I was born, but my elder sisters report that he was a highly satisfactory grandparent who always had time for little children, and a marvellous fund of stories. They had heard nothing of the hints I picked up from time to time from conversations overheard between my mother and her contemporaries, of his being cavalier about running up debts and leaving them for my father to settle, or of his being touched with the sort of wanderlust which women have always found baleful.

And from an old friend of the family from The Early Days I once heard that my grandfather was a truly diminutive man—in comparison my father, who stood 5 feet 2 inches, was a fine figure of a man—who had one of the most musical baritone speaking voices a man might encounter in a lifetime, and that he could curse with it as steadily and rhythmically and with less boring repetition than anyone my informant (by then in his sixties) had ever encountered.

My parents' families had been acquainted in Iowa. I have heard my mother and Mrs Mildmay, in some unguarded moment when they were unaware of the presence of little pitchers with big ears, debating the degree to which my grandfather had been responsible for the untimely death of his young wife. She had been tubercular, and had been warned, when my father was born, that another pregnancy would be fatal. She was pregnant again almost immediately, however, and died, leaving my father as her only, unremembering, issue. As birth control at that time meant strict continence, her husband was held to have sacrificed his wife to his 'appetites'. Apparently my grandfather had accepted this verdict himself. My father once said that his earliest recollection, from a time when he was hardly more than a toddler, was of 'helping' his father to put some milk cows into

8

a corral. He thought that his father must have tossed a stone at a cow, who dodged, leaving my father in the line of fire. What he could remember clearly was being gathered into his father's arms and hearing him cry out, 'My God! My God! I killed my wife, and now I've killed the boy too!'

I believe though that he lived little of his childhood with his father; that his father came and went from his life, which he spent at first with a grandmother who spoke mostly German. He remembered occasional German words and phrases, and one of the few subjects which could move him to lyricism was 'sow-belly and sauerkraut'. But Aunt Laura took him over before he was very old, so I suppose the grandmother died too. My father was devoted to Aunt Laura. She did not marry until after he had grown and left the nest, and her husband did not live long after their marriage. She was left with one child, their daughter Ruby.

During the period of the tightest currency restrictions of the Second World War my father, then in his seventies, received a letter from a lawyer in Chicago who had handled Aunt Laura's business over the years. She had been found, more than ninety years old, paralysed, incoherent and dying, in the bedroom of an otherwise empty house in Chicago when the new owners, who had bought it for cash a few days previously, moved in. By what means no one knows Ruby had obtained, only a few days before, her mother's signature to a document giving herself legal ownership of all of her mother's property. She had liquidated every scrap of it immediately for cash, and vanished without trace. Aunt Laura's lawyer, searching through such papers as he could find, decided that my father's correspondence seemed to offer the best hope of help for the dying woman outside the chill embrace of city welfare. My father made prodigious efforts to get enough American dollars to visit Chicago, or at least money to provide decent care for her, but being neither greedy nor insecure he had never cultivated the peddlers of privilege. He had finally to content himself with dispatch of an impressive document, complete with substantial testimonials, wherein he undertook to guarantee all reasonable medical and burial disbursements made on Aunt Laura's behalf, payment to be made as soon as currency regulations should permit, and

9

binding his heirs to settle the debt from his estate should he die before it could be settled.

In his youth my father finished his schooling in Iowa, went to college, qualified as a teacher and then went west to Oregon, where he was teaching when the Spanish-American War broke out. He enlisted and went to the Philippines. He had many mild and unwarlike reminiscences of that period, of army friends and incidents. He never ceased to be surprised by his discovery that the small, spare, unbustling men like himself had endured the heat and long marches and burden packing better than big, conspicuously muscular men. Only once, and that some fifty years after the event, did my father mention any actual fighting that had taken place, and that came upon us not as an anecdote but as a sudden vivid act of total recall, with even the sweat beading his brow at the appropriate moment. He suddenly became again one of an advance party slogging along, not really expecting or thinking about trouble, who stumbled on to some Filipino soldiers who had held their fire, evidently hoping to remain undiscovered. There had been no time to shoot. My father rushed his man with his bayonet. Whether the Americans then advanced or retreated I forget, but he did not know the fate of the Filipino soldier, only that there was blood on his bayonet afterwards. He told this with neither relish nor regret, but with the astonishment with which the incident had obviously filled him half a century earlier.

It seemed a good time, so I asked him then why the Spanish-American War had been fought. He looked so puzzled that I recast the question: 'Why did the Americans fight the Filipinos?'

It was obvious that he thought the question irrelevant. When he did finally reply it was with a rare trace of irritability.

'They didn't know what they wanted. The Filipinos didn't know what was good for them.'

An anonymous State Department spokesman could hardly have prepared a better statement. . . .

STATE DEPARTMENT, however, was out of the question. He was invalided out of his war on full pension, so wracked by malaria and dysentery that he was not expected to be a prolonged burden on the American taxpayer. The doctors, unable to cure his condition, recommended an outdoor life in a cold climate as his best hope of survival.

And so, in company with his father, he came north into Canada in 1901. There the transcontinental railways had opened up the last of the agricultural lands, which must have been almost as empty, awaiting the homesteaders, as the garden of Eden. The buffalo herds had already been exterminated. The Indians had been conned on to their reservations, the world's most venerable Displaced Persons camps.

My father came to the railhead, which stood then at Red Deer, by train. From there he and his father, with their beasts and wagons, set off. The land they finally settled on was some seventy miles from Red Deer as the crow flies, but as they were not travelling by crow they estimated their semi-annual trips for supplies to be perhaps ninety miles each way, and allowed not days, but weeks, for the return journey.

They must have crossed quite a number of unstaked homesteads which would have seemed to offer advantages over the one they finally settled on. Even during the drought, which was the period at which I knew the farm best, a considerable percentage of it was under water all of the time, with even more water enough of the time to make it unfit for cultivation and of little value for grazing or hay. And as 1901 was in the midst of a very wet cycle of years, even more of it—perhaps as much as a quarter, all told—must have been permanently under water. Roughly another quarter of the land was wooded, offering little grazing and requiring laborious clearing before it could be planted. The woods were of no value beyond providing fuel and a little shelter for the livestock, and poles from which temporary straw-wadded sheds could be made. Poplar, willow, cottonwoods, the occasional birch, saskatoon, chokecherry, pincherry . . . the usual tough, meagre trees of the parklands. Difficult land to cultivate, mediocre land for grazing: an odd choice, in an almost empty land. It never occurred to me, though, to question it when I lived there, or even when he was alive. And since he lived with his choice without regret for more than half a century he presumably chose well. He didn't like the flat treeless plains, so much easier to cultivate. He liked hills and lakes and variety in landscape. Upon occasion he used the word 'pretty'—a wildly aesthetic performance for that time and place. It may be that he liked to see his water supply and fuel visible and abundant about him. And he would in any event have been proof against lotus lands, had any been going thereabouts. For although he was a cheerful man of even temper, and gave off no odour of gratuitous austerity, he had a thorough instinctive mistrust of all fast bucks, all easy money, all short cuts to wealth and/or the millennium. Feeling the *hubris* suspended over Easy Street he could pass through it unimpressed, unself-righteous even, and whistle his way back to the semi-desirable farm which would yield a living if you treated it right, but never much more than a living.

When he settled on that place there were only two families living within a radius of maybe ten miles: the Van Dykes and the Losies. They may well have been genuine frontiersmen. Their names are only names to me, for the tidal wave of homesteaders, of which my father was a herald, seems to have pushed them on to some farther perimeter of civilization. I think that I once saw Mrs Van Dyke, like something out of Fenimore Cooper, dressed in a long dress of some dark stuff that wouldn't show the dirt, with matching poke-bonnet, enthroned on the boot box in the corner of our kitchen, smoking her corncob pipe—but the 'memory' may be fantasy. Our childish imaginations were much stirred by the oddity of a woman smoking a corncob pipe— although that seemed an outlandish rather than an immoral matter, as cigarette smoking by women was still considered to be in our part of the world in those days.

I cannot recall my father ever speaking of the illness that sent him to Canada—indeed, I learned of it only when I asked my mother why he quit school-teaching and came to Canada. He must have made a fairly spectacular recovery. During my own lifetime I cannot recall his spending a day in bed—or even lying in for a few hours of a morning—until the day of his final collapse into coma and death.

He throve on pioneering, its solitudes and neighbourliness, its challenges and simplicities. He even enjoyed his father's cooking, although it always sounded spectacular rather than edible. So unskilled was my grandfather that, when they first settled down to their diet, which consisted mostly of beans, rice, salt pork and prunes, he began his first essay into the preparation of rice by half filling a very large pot with rice and adding water. His subsequent frantic efforts to find enough containers to keep up with the expansion of the rice provided my father with decades of merriment. It was just as well, as my mother did not join him until ten years later.

By that time Mafeking had come into existence on a new railway line a mere eighteen miles away (still as the crow flew), so they needed only a couple of days to make their trips for supplies. And they had built themselves a house of unseasoned softwood lumber from the nearest sawmill, and tin sheeting and shingles and tarpaper, and had scooped a cellar out of the earth beneath it to store food in. Downstairs was one room, kitchen-cum-living-room. The loft above, unheated, had been divided into two miniscule bedrooms.

To this my mother came in February 1911.

'Married in black, you'll wish yourself back. . . .' Her wedding dress was, as it happened, a compromise: she was in mourning for a recently deceased parent, and settled for a fine black-and-white check taffeta trimmed with white lace. Photography seems not to have penetrated to Mafeking at that time, and so there was no wedding picture, but she must have looked well in that dress. The tight-laced waists and long bouffant skirts of the period flattered her short, rather pear-shaped figure. A snapshot taken of her not too long before shows abundant black hair piled high into an attractive bun (she was the only member of her family to escape mousey hair), a good, clear, firm profile, good complexion and an alert, lively, good-humoured expression.

When I first tried to visualize my mother's reaction to her new Canadian home I thought that she must surely have looked upon it with a sinking heart. It must have looked little more than a shed, there under the blinding limitless shimmer of a February noon, or the magnificent unimaginable and uninhabitable arctic blues of a February evening. But she was probably fairly well prepared for the physical environment. My father would have

13

sent adequate descriptions of conditions in his letters. The curtainless windows, the walls innocent of paint or paper, the coarse grey blankets (some of which were still extant as saddle blankets in my day), the splintery wooden floors, bare even of linoleum and so cold that the tracked-in snow would just lie there, unmelting: to that bride, already in her early thirties after a decade of long-distance wooing, they probably seemed so many challenges to be tackled with zest. And my father must—even he!—have offered a little honeymooning before absent-mindedness and books set in.

Within a few years two tiny houses which had belonged to departed pioneers were hauled up and tacked on to the existing three rooms. These, which were roofed with tarpaper, would become sieves in a matter of minutes during a brisk hailstorm. It was as well that we lived in a sort of narrow corridor between two hail-prone belts, for although my father always had a vague intention of putting cedar shingles on those roofs in place of the tarpaper, nothing came of it. Indeed for a considerable time he intended, I believe, to build a new house for my mother. When I was very small there was still a book of potted house plans lying around, but I think she was already communing with it more as the reliquary of deceased dreams than as imminent possibility, for 1929 was already past and Hard Times were upon us. I know that her choice had fallen upon one with dormer windows upstairs, and a dining-room separate from the kitchen, and with a proper basement in which a furnace, to heat the whole of the house, could have been installed.

In 1911 she had probably accepted cheerfully enough all those temporary discomforts, inconveniences and compromise solutions.

Forty-five years and seven children later they were still there, grown into her world.

THE HOMESTEADERS from America arrived several years earlier on our scene than those from Europe, most of whom did not come until the First World War, so only about a third of the homesteads were inhabited around the time of my mother's arrival. She had always taken pride in being of the pioneer generation, and could speak with a certain nostalgia of The Early Days. On the whole she must have accepted cheerfully enough the hardships and deprivations she had bargained for in advance. She missed her friends sorely though. She was inclined to blame the womenfolk amongst whom she found herself, especially the Scandinavian women, of whom many hardly set foot off their own farms, while some lived all their adult lives and bore all their children in Canada, never learning enough English to carry on a simple conversation once their slender stock of polite greetings had been exhausted. However, I don't think she realized how age and family responsibilities diminish one's capacity as well as opportunities for other intimacies. And in fact she got on little better with the women of American or English origin than with the Swedes and Norwegians. It is probable that her most satisfactory relationship in our immediate neighbourhood was with Mrs Varma, another American, with whom she competed for the role of principal bell-wether. They were richly magisterial towards one another. Once the party-line telephone was installed they spent hours monitoring one another's conversations, and indignantly accusing one another of doing just that. They spoke their telephone conversations in codes and riddles to mystify one another. It was enjoyable enough, in its own way, but it was not intimacy.

But, regardless of her discontents, my mother never quite lost track of the fact that things could have been a lot worse. She had a good deal of respect for my father, and appreciated his virtues, even if she never quite got over his defects. And, of course, there was always the lot of those Scandinavian women to contemplate. Their men would have lost face by doing a lot of the heavier and more disagreeable outdoor chores, and so the women had to do those—milk the cows, harness and unharness the work-horses, for instance—as well as keeping the poultry, the garden, the house, and child-bearing and -rearing. It might have been all right in the Old Country, where a family had three or four cows and a couple of horses, but the families in our neighbourhood milked fifteen to thirty cows during the depression when, for weeks and months on end, their entire tiny cash income came from the cream and egg sales; and most families could and did put at least eight horses into the field almost daily from the time of the spring thaws until winter freeze-up. In our neighbourhood, at least, if you had to be a woman it did not pay to be one whose native tongue was not English: your chances of longevity decreased dramatically. The Mrs Dahlbergs and Mrs Thorsons and Mrs Sjostroms and Mrs Schmaltzes died years before their husbands, in their late thirties, forties or early fifties. The women of English or American origin all seemed to live to their threescore and ten, if not more. One might possibly have been able to compute a farm woman's chance of survival to a venerable age by her flower-beds. The cultivation of flowers was one of the few gratuitous, frivolous, artistic activities a farm woman had—her holiday from necessity. How those pinks and sweet-williams, columbines and lilacs were watched over, seeds collected and exchanged, slips started in pots! Their tiny brightnesses were a gallant impertinence under that vast indifferent sky and hostile climate. Where the women spoke no English and died young there were almost no flower-beds. Mrs Erikson, the only one of our Swedish neighbours to outlive her husband (and who went on and on living, as though determined to compensate for all those who hadn't managed to) was the only local Scandinavian immigrant woman to grow flowers.

Fortunately my mother did have one friend from 'down home' who lived some fourteen miles away. Once the Model T Ford had packed up, visits to the Mildmays, which had to be sandwiched between some three hours of solid chores at either end of the day, were rare and complicated, but we still managed them some three or four times a year. Mrs Mildmay and my mother had known each other from childhood and had hosts of mutual acquaintances, shared remembrances of things past and brought each other up to date on such current gossip as had filtered through to them.

It was in concert with Mrs Mildmay that my mother inadvertently (for, as usual, I had not forced awareness of my presence upon them) opened up a mysterious and shadowy world, and

16

hidden depths within their own seemingly transparent selves. They spoke of Roman Catholicism. Previously I had thought of Roman Catholicism, if at all, as just another church. We were accustomed to variety in churches. We were United Church of Canada, there was a Lutheran Church ten miles north at Cross Creeks, and infrequent Church of England services were held in Regalia. There was no Roman Catholic Church nearer than Mafeking, and I had heard little of it, good or ill. But when my mother and Mrs Mildmay spoke of the Catholics it was with a furtive excitement utterly unlike their attitudes towards other churches. They spoke not a word of transubstantiation, nor of the nature of the Trinity, nor of Mariolatry, the communion of saints nor the apostolic succession. They spoke of the goings-on in convents, of the uses made by the priesthood of its access to convents. . . .

In later years when I became acquainted with Roman Catholics I suffered some initial shock because they were so ordinary; and their priests were a great anticlimax. I must have invested them with near-magical powers—to cast the evil eye, to hypnotize the will with some instant secret rite—I know not what. . . . I suppose that the Church's perpetual harping on celibacy and chastity and the sins of the flesh had, logically enough, provided a focus for the sexual anxieties and taboos of that Protestant Middle West wherein my mother and Mrs Mildmay had been formed.

I can recall no other manifestation of anti-Catholicism in that community—if, indeed, 'anti' ought to be used of sentiments so ambivalent. I never heard of any insult being offered to any lay Catholic (indeed my mother's anti-Catholicism, like her Anglophobia, excluded all the individuals we knew personally). Curiously enough, my mother made no attempt that I know of to initiate any of her children into this taboo, but left it to us to find for ourselves such symbols as should serve us in this alien land.

There would seem to have been little necessity for us to provide ourselves with any taboos at all. We were an uncrowded, egalitarian, potentially wealthy society, blessed with universal education and a technology already visibly headed for sophistication. In a community of such mixed origins as ours everyone might claim to be 'different', so that difference was normal.

Gradations in wealth or opportunity were not very remarkable, and there was no established higher or lower class to invest with those characteristics which cause the most pain, humiliation and anxiety. The ancestral Christian scapegoat, the Jew, was not to be found in our midst. The native Indian was hardly more so, and anyhow his subjection was so complete as to shield him from that victimization which is compounded, in part, by fear generated by the potency and power attributed to the victim. There were no Negroes, beyond an insignificant straggle in the cities.

The immigration laws thoughtfully, if perhaps inadvertently, offered a solution. Quantities of Chinese were admitted to perform the ungrateful labours of laundry and café. All but a sprinkling of wives and families, however, were deliberately excluded, not out of fear that they would become indigent burdens upon the community, but out of an instinct to deny their virility and fertility. Even I, as a child in the middle of an immensity of under-populated prairie parkland, had heard of 'golden hordes' and 'yellow peril'. I can't think where I heard of these things—for all I know the geese flying south in October trumpeted them over the land.

Anyhow, here, scattered thinly all over the west of North America, was a supply of men forced into celibacy or into temporary liaisons with white women who had, already, for one reason or another, found themselves so far beyond the pale of society that they had nothing to lose. Whatever slender ties the Chinese would have made would be slipped off, and he would return to the bosom of his ancestors, to the wife and adult children he might not have seen for thirty or forty years—back to the family whose living sacrifice he had been throughout those years.

For living sacrifice is what those men must have been. They were the point at which the famous hospitality and neighbourliness stopped. There was not a white remittance-man shiftless or unwashed enough not to receive at least one invitation to eat his Christmas dinner with a proper family, but thousands of Chinese must have lived in our midst decade after decade without ever seeing the inside of a white Christian's home. Theirs but to launder, cook, wash dishes, listen to the kids shouting 'Chinky Chinky Chinaman, sitting on a rail', and send money home to the family. In a tiny town like Regalia there would be but one Chinese, or at most two. Annually, on the occasion of the Chinese New Year, they would close up shop for three or four days and congregate for the festival. Then back to their isolations, their unbelievably long hours of toil, with not even the luxury of a ghetto. Yet I never heard of one cracking up or taking to drink.

They were seldom actually persecuted. The children sauced them only from a discreet distance, and they would not be the only target for the children by any manner of means. Most adults spoke to them civilly enough most of the time. But if a community had some questionable activities to perform it would quite likely 'requisition' the premises of the Chinese for that purpose. Regalia's more or less permanent poker game lived in the back room of the Chinese restaurant. I don't know that gambling was illegal: it was most certainly furtive. Men found it easier to behave discreditably in the presence of the Chinese than in the presence of men they regarded as their peers. He was the outsider to whose judgment one might remain indifferent. In towns large enough to sport a red-light district it was often almost synonymous with Chinatown, not because the Chinese were actively implicated in prostitution, but because, given half a chance, a portion of the white population would cocoon the Chinese in their midst in their own more malodorous fantasies and practices. He was surrounded by a folklore of the opium den and white slave traffic—a most curious epilogue to the Opium Wars! It did a woman no good to be seen hanging about the Chinese restaurant, even in such an uneventful hamlet as Regalia. The wives of respectable farmers waited out their tedious waits for their husbands in the general store, not at the café.

In my youth it was still possible to enjoy a sensation of living dangerously simply by devouring chow mein and noodles in a clean and efficient restaurant. This may well have had something to do with the spoliation endured by the Canadians of Japanese origin during the Second World War (not too much distinction being made by the white races between Japanese and Chinese), although the Germans in our midst were left in peace. But laws and customs change: I believe that Canadians of Asian origin have, of late, found a more comfortable, prosaic role.

But well after the end of that war, in a little town in the Peace

River country which had preserved its aura of pioneering innocence intact, I witnessed the baiting of the Chinaman by half a
dozen young men, at least two of whom were old enough to be
sporting military discharge buttons.

They stood at his counter, dawdling over their coffee,
watching the rain bucket down outside, bored, horseplaying,
kidding the Chinese behind his till and his round, steel-rimmed
spectacles. Without diminishing the good nature in their voices
they started competing with one another to ask him the most
outrageous questions about his sex life. Did he have a wife in
China? One wife! He probably had half a dozen! I mean—just
look at him! What good would *one* woman be to a fine figure of a
man like that? Why, he must stand all of five foot three in his
stockinged feet! One woman wouldn't be able to take it for
long, now would she? Be worn right out. . . . Did they do it the
same in China? How did he feel about all that nice white meat
that came into his café, eh? Passed through his hands, you might
say. . . . Well, he must feel a bit of a tingle sometimes, didn't
he. . . ?

Ad nauseam.

They seemed fond of him, after their fashion. They loaded
him with their crude fears and fantasies as if he were a heaven-
sent camel. Perhaps they were even obscurely grateful to him,
for all I know.

The Chinese kept his glassy, paralytic smile intact, but nothing
inscrutable was happening behind those unlovely, steel-rimmed
spectacles.

Murder.

If he is not dead by now he has probably returned whence he
came, to Hong Kong, to China itself—one more ambassador
between our two great civilizations, et cetera.

M Y FATHER named our local school an elegant Spanish name, last faint echo of the Spanish-American War. The locals promptly anglicized it, stripping it thus of any unseemly elegance and, happily, it is unlikely that any of them took the trouble to discover that through its utterance they were rendering an aesthetic judgment on the scenery.

But before naming the school he had had to provide most of the impetus for getting it built and financed. However, as his belief in education was as firm as his sense of civic responsibility, the chores involved were probably welcome enough. The school was a going concern before any of his own children were old enough to attend it.

Jimmy Price, its first teacher, was a man who had a good deal in common with my father, including the same sort of sense of humour and the same love for books and book learning. He boarded with our family during his two years of teaching there, and then went away to study law and to set up in practice several hundred miles away. He and my father always kept in touch, though, until my father died, and his letters were always a particular source of pleasure.

He visited us once when I was little. I was upstairs in bed when he came. I got up, I remember, and glued my eye to the knot-hole in the floor which, with luck, afforded a glimpse into what was going on in the kitchen, but I didn't manage to catch sight of him that night, only heard his deep rumble of laughter answering to my father's tenor laugh.

Next morning when I came downstairs the grown-ups had almost finished their breakfast, and I sat down to the table just as they rose. I had lived all of my young life among the lean stringy men who eat often and ravenously, but who work it all off. Jimmy Price, when he pushed his chair back from the table, displayed the first splendid, unrepentant belly I ever saw. It seemed to me—memory must exaggerate—that he pushed his chair back and pushed his chair back, and still there was belly to be extracted from under the table. He exuded a *joie de vivre* of which, I believe, my mother felt a little disapproving.

There is a curious little postscript to this essentially un-remarkable association of two men who met through a shared belief in education. Jimmy Price's daughter and I went to university at the same time more than thirty years later. We saw little of each other. We were not pursuing the same studies, and she was younger than I. I had the good fortune to be among the post-war 'veterans', having knocked about earning my living for a few years before going to university. We could dispense with the more childish frolics of the campus without feeling either cheated of life's goodies or queer as three-dollar bills. We could even take our studies reasonably seriously—as distinct from merely trying to get good marks in them—if we wanted to. Things were not necessarily so simple, though, even at that period, for the student who came to the university direct from high school.

One night I most earnestly wanted the use of a typewriter, my antique having collapsed under me in mid essay, and I remembered that Pat Price, who lived just down the corridor from me, had one. So, rather late and unannounced, I barged in on her. I found her in a state of damp, exhausted, tearful despair. She wasn't sorry to see me, really, once the initial embarrassment was over. It wasn't as if we moved in the same circles. And then my five extra years probably made me seem middle-aged to her. (That was the year when a fellow student, on learning that I was twenty-three, gasped, 'My, you carry your age well!')

Pat stumbled and fumbled and bumbled about for a while before she could finally bring herself to be unburdened of the awful truth: well, she thought she *must* be—after all, each of her friends at university had a boy friend, or were plotting to get one, or made pathetic jokes about not having one—were, in short, normal, eternally male-conscious. They talked endlessly of clubs and 'frats' and clothes and dates. Pat did not find this interesting. She didn't throb to the nearness of a single male of her acquaintance. In fact, she was actually *interested* in the law which she was studying. She had meant to be her father's partner, and eventually to take over his practice. But now . . . she didn't know what was wrong with her. Perhaps she was Lesbian? Frigid? Only one thing was certain: life was quite insupportable.

Actually her chances of finding a fellow student who would not have solemnly agreed with her diagnosis were not all that considerable by my reckoning, and so the fact that it was my typewriter and none other which had given up the ghost at that precise moment may possibly be classified as a very minor miracle. For I thought it far more likely that Pat belonged at a university, whereas a good many of her friends probably did not. There is an absence of *débutanterie* or similar acceptable bourgeois mating agencies, and so a lot of charming and attractive young ladies with no scholarly ambitions whatsoever are packed off to the universities where they are exposed to the contemporary crop of the most eligible young males. I suppose there is no real reason why a university should not be used in this way, but although I was myself only a middling scholar, I felt strongly that it was all right to use the university for study. I said so firmly, cheerfully and (as it was late and my essay, which was due first thing in the morning, was yet to be typed out) briskly, and asked for the loan of her typewriter. She cheered up and gave it to me.

Our paths crossed no more frequently thereafter than before, and so I was astonished a few years later when I was about to be married to receive a generous cheque as a gift from her father, along with a note saying that he believed I did not know that I had in fact prevented Pat from carrying through a heartbroken resolve to quit the university for which she had decided she was unfit!

In one generation we had progressed from our parents' simple-minded belief in education to the point where a university student could be paralysed by shame and grief through the discovery that she had a mind which liked exercise.

Anyhow, Pat took her degree, articled, became her father's partner, eventually married another lawyer and, when last I heard, was expecting the first little tort—or whatever it is that mated lawyers have.

My father's involvement with education did not end when the schoolhouse had been built and named. It is likely that he was secretary-treasurer to the school board from the beginning; certainly, by the time I became aware that such a post existed, he had been filling it for a time which, to my eyes, stretched away back into the mists of antiquity.

All of his public works, modest and parochial as they were, he performed with a conscious dignity and decorum. It was with a slight air of solemn occasion that, on a winter's evening, he produced his 'books' and spread them out on the oilcloth of the kitchen table, and brought forth the bottle of red ink which was kept exclusively for the book-keeping. At such times our homework seemed kid stuff indeed, compared with the stern realities of the school board.

He carried on this unpaid work year after year—perhaps a quarter of a century in all. During the latter years I was myself involved in it in a small way; when I was the only one from our house still attending the school I was from time to time entrusted with a sealed envelope for the teacher, a burden which filled me with pride and, until it was safely delivered, anxiety. (As a child I lost and mislaid things; as an adult I still do.) I knew, although I was not supposed to know, that the teacher's pay cheque was inside.

The years of devoted service did not go entirely unnoticed by the community. The day came when the teacher complained—not to the school board, actually, but loosely around the neighbourhood—that she was not being paid regularly, or in full. In a sudden surge of hitherto dormant civic zeal some of our neighbours organized a public meeting to which my father was summoned, and during which the possibility was bandied about that he might have mismanaged public funds—or worse. . . .

Why anyone should have hurried into such an accusation is puzzling, for in 1935–7, which was about when this incident must have taken place, a man needed a good memory to recall when he had last paid more than a token amount towards his taxes. Even the most affluent turned out to do road work, repair telephone lines—anything and everything which would serve in part in lieu of cash payment of taxes. Cash, like the normal seasonal rainfall, had simply disappeared mysteriously and completely from our lives, and to a considerable extent we were back on a barter economy. Our teacher might have considered herself privileged to receive even erratic partial salary; there were large sections of the country, harder hit by drought and depression than our own, where in return for her services a teacher received no more than food and shelter, and she would have to move from one household to the next every few weeks, for no family could spare food for an extra mouth over an extended period. My father's accusers had certainly not discharged their tax arrears: they might at least have made some inquiries before assuming that there was, by some miracle, anything in the education kitty to be mismanaged or misappropriated.

My father had no difficulty in proving that he had not only paid over every penny he received towards the teacher's salary but also that he had, over a considerable period of time, made her an occasional small allowance out of his own personal overdraft, an obligation which his natural chivalry had prevented his making known to her.

It would be pleasant to think that his detractors had been pleased and relieved to find his integrity intact, but your scandalmonger, like your typhoid bacillus, is ill served by clean hands. . . .

It was not long after this time that my father resigned from his work with the school board, but I cannot say whether as a result of this incident or simply because the substantial administrative changes made in the school system throughout the province rendered the whole school board obsolete. Certainly not many years later our school and hundreds of others like it were closed down, and buses collected the children and took them to much larger consolidated schools.

My father was also a municipal councillor during almost the same long period. In this connection he made Long Distance Telephone Calls, which he did with commendable casualness, considering the awe they inspired in us. It was not easy to be casual, considering the primitive state of the telephones and lines. A great deal of shouting was needed for sending a message, and absolute silence for receiving one. Sometimes, when the call was incoming, invisible and nameless neighbours had to be importuned to stop listening in and hang up, as the sound faded as more receivers were off the hook. And then there were trips to Imperia, thirteen miles away. Most of the meetings were held during the winter—I suppose there was no getting farmers to turn out to meetings when the weather was suitable for farm work—and it seemed that the summons to a meeting was almost invariably accompanied by two or three days of the north wind which piled mountains of snow over eleven of those thirteen miles. Often, even when he had stopped overnight in Imperia to rest them, the horses would be stumbling with exhaustion by the time he returned home.

His role as municipal councillor ended roughly the same time as the work for the school board. After years of being re-elected by acclamation there came a bitterly fought election. He had been one of the most enthusiastic members of the council when it had decided to put the municipality under a liability to support the hospital in Mafeking out of the rates. The hospital, the only one within a radius of forty miles, was in desperate financial straits at the time, I believe. Hospital ratepayers received treatment at drastically lower fees than non-ratepayers, but suddenly every taxpayer was seized with an unshakable conviction that he and his family were destined to live without illness for ever and ever, bowed down under the additional tax. My father was dropped from the council.[1]

This must almost have coincided with the advent of Social Credit in the province, with its promise to save us all by issuing lots of paper dollars or Deutschmarks or whatever. Their landslide victory finally convinced my father, I believe, that the human race was idiot beyond remedy. He retired, grumbling briefly and mildly, into private citizenship, and stayed there.

MY MOTHER, like all of her family, was very church-going. My father could have borne it had Sunday lived up to its reputation as a day of rest: he usually slept through the sermon (maintaining indignantly that he had heard every word of it), but he could, as he knew, have slept better at home. However, he never questioned my mother's inalienable right to expose herself and her offspring to organized

[1] The ratepayers still, however, support the hospital in Mafeking.

The author's grandmother, who died soon after this portrait was made

Her son, the author's father, in the uniform worn during the Spanish-American War

religion. He grumbled a little, usually caused us to be a little late but not shockingly so, and allowed us to be faithful.

From the halcyon days—the Model T Ford days—comes a dim souvenir of church and Sunday school as genuine social occasions; of so many people gossiping from cluster to cluster after service that the visiting seemed as ample and lengthy as the service itself. There were sub-Pre-Raphaelite religious picture cards for tots like myself. There were other pictorial incentives to pious moppets: sylvan scenes upon which bunnies or lambs or bluebirds were glued to reward good attendance or verses committed to memory. Competition was fierce.

But who were the pious infant rivals? And what happened to their devotion? For before I had really sorted out the pattern of the halcyon days both the days and those congregations were gone. There was no more Sunday school, and even church services seemed fewer—only two Sundays a month. And often—in fact usually—my family was the entire congregation.

The services were conducted by a succession of ministers who deserve, I believe, to be called heroic. They had to travel anything up to forty miles on a Sunday in a rattletrap, unheated car over unpaved, ungravelled roads which, never good, were often nightmares of mud, dust or drifted snow, to hold three or four services with small, shabby, undistinguished gatherings in cold, dingy halls or schools. No hierarchy offered security, ready promotion or a chance of rubbing cassocks with a colourful or fashionable bishop. There was no glamour of vestments or stained glass, or even tolerable music. Wealthy city churches were few and far between. They shared the hard times with us—having of course to present a veneer of gentility with which we were not burdened: they *had* to be the Joneses. It must have been hell for their self-effacing wives. The poverty of the Franciscans has an aesthetic rightness which makes it pleasing even to the Hollywood box-office, where the perhaps greater poverty and sacrifice of the poor Protestant family man, uncushioned from the world, beset by the legitimate needs of his dependants, raises a giggle. My brothers and I thought it a joke that the Rev. Tapp had difficulty in saying prayers year after year. His false teeth had been fitted prematurely, and the gums continued to shrink; whenever he bowed his head he was in danger of losing

C

his teeth, and had to punctuate his effusions with audible clicks. Being a poor man with a large family he could not afford new teeth. Regardless of the man's piety, that's hardly a role that Bing Crosby would croon his way through.

But if in fact any of those modest and admirable gentlemen was actually holy he was successfully reticent about it—like the United Church of Canada itself. It originated in a compromise between Methodist and Presbyterian in which the evangelical fire of Methodism and the apocalyptic ferocious logic of the Presbyterian were jettisoned. There remained a soggy mess of vague, good-natured nothing much—a best buy for the consumer who wishes to cut down on his religious intake. It is not a Church to incite rebellion. When I belonged to its ranks I never encountered anyone, so far as I know, sporting the stigmata of religious suffering, nor anyone whose moral muscles bulged from wrestling with the obstacles to salvation. I don't really know what we thought of God. I never heard His Name or His supposed Will invoked in any crisis or to settle any problem or argument. If He had had to be brought in it would, I suppose, have been much like summoning the minister, which would only have been done after the mess was cleared up, emotions under control, a clean tablecloth laid and some sort of decent hospitality prepared for his reception. And this, in my experience, would have been the normal attitude in members of the congregation of the United Church—a total absence of anything which might be called otherworldly.

I woke up one morning knowing that I did not believe in eternal personal salvation, nor in any other of the basic tenets of Christianity, and realizing that I probably never *had* believed in them but had simply never got around to examining myself on the subject before. I was lonely at first, being apparently the only person I knew who knew herself to be agnostic (I didn't even know the word for it, at the time), although I reckoned the great majority of my acquaintances were just as agnostic as I, only they'd never noticed.

Although I had left home and been independent for some time, I felt that I ought to tell my mother about this (to me) soul-shaking discovery. I felt that she had a right to know, even if I doubted if she would be very understanding. Indeed as the day for exposition approached I dreaded her reaction. I didn't know whether it would be shock, anger or hurt, but I was quite certain that it would be fiercely something.

I had never discussed religion with my mother. Casual, or even earnest, talk of such matters outside the church service and between lay persons might even strike her as unseemly. However, I did manage to broach the subject and to explain plainly and undramatically that I could no longer believe in either the truth or relevance of Christianity, that I had stopped going to church, but that I would not embarrass her by refusing to attend services with the family when I was at home. She greeted this information with a vigorous but brief snort of disapproval and, to my astonishment, let the matter drop. Indeed so little impression had I made that some years later, after I had been abroad in parts traditionally classified as 'heathen' for what she had evidently decided was a vintage year, she informed me that she had suggested to the programme convenors of the local Women's Missionary Society that I might be available to speak. She was even somewhat surprised when I refused.

Yet when I asked her casually, and I trust tactfully, not to include me among those near and dear to her who receive every Christmas a year's subscription to the *Reader's Digest*, the reaction was equally astonishing. I suggested that I would prefer lingerie or stockings or bath oil—a list which hardly reeks of intellectual deviousness. But she pounced upon that suggestion like a terrier; she got it by the throat, threw it into the air and broke its neck, worried it into bloody shreds and was careful to bury it amongst the retrievable bones whence it is exhumed for examination and comment from time to time. I must this time have transgressed against the Living Word.

Which asserts, unless I am mistaken, that *Yes, there is a Santa Claus*. . . .

THERE WASN'T much about in the way of crime. Theft was unknown. We didn't have a key for our door, and I doubt if anyone in our district would have locked the door when going out. Such violence as there was—or was suspected—seemed to begin, like charity, at home, and did not become a public or police matter.

But there must have been a period of alcohol prohibition, probably corresponding roughly to the Noble Experiment to the south of the border, for a considerable quantity of minor legends had gathered on the subject of a home brew, known as 'moonshine'.

Just a few miles to the west of us is a belt of light sandy soil, and during the drought it would bear nothing but buckbush and indigenous scrub trees. Upon it all labour was futile and so it attracted, as by a magnet, the Jensen tribe, who apparently believed honest toil to be but vanity and vexation of spirit. Some of the tribe had married and reproduced themselves, others remained bachelors, but all of them lived a shiftless, Dog Patch existence. They turned naturally enough to the manufacture of moonshine.

One of our favourite bits of folklore was of the visit paid to Knut and Ole Jensen by the Mountie from Imperia, who took an uncommon interest in the boilerful of mash that was simmering peacefully on their stove. He asked what it was, and was told that it was pig feed. He inquired after the recipe, and was told that it was just barley chop, potato peelings and other domestic waste being cooked into a tasty mess. The Mountie borrowed a spoon, and stirred it, and was very impressed. He said that the Jensen pigs were fortunate pigs indeed. And then he sat down.

They talked for a long time—a very long time—of this and that. Knut and Ole inquired, obliquely, as to why their uninvited guest stayed so long, and wondered why pressing business did not require him to depart, but he said that he reckoned to wait and see those pigs fed. He had never known farmers so thoughtful as to purchase raisins and I know not what-all just to make pig mash palatable, and he was naturally curious to see whether or not the pigs were properly appreciative. At length all conversation and alternatives to conversation were exhausted, and the mash was fed to the surprised and delighted porkers. Upon which the Mountie made his farewells, and another crime wave bit the dust. . . .

I believe that the Mounties from both Imperia and Mafeking were interested in Albert Brown at one period too. The Browns were our nearest neighbours. Albert too was connected with moonshine, but in the distributing rather than the manufacturing side, and he was generally credited with being pretty wild in his youth. But before I was old enough to savour the excitement properly Prohibition must have ended—certainly moonshine was a thing of the past—and Albert had not only married but had fathered a couple of children and got religion—one of the way-out evangelical varieties—upon which he forsook his wife and children to become an itinerant preacher. Even the church-going people did not take warmly to this development, regardless of the relevant texts, and reproached him for the hardship he was inflicting upon his dependants. He always replied that the Lord would provide for them. His father, a brusque, hard-working man who literally saved them from starvation, used to say with feeling that he wished the Lord would either be more forth-coming when the grocery bills were presented or else would stop taking all the credit.

On the whole the Mounties remained remarkably remote from us, becoming neither reassuring protective figures nor the target for aggression and tension. Neither Hollywood nor the tourist bureaus nor the Chambers of Commerce could promote them into popular sentimentality. Next to the Chinese the Mounties, with their prolonged para-military celibacy, must have been about the most solitary men in the country, especially those in one-man posts like Imperia.

Perhaps it will lighten their burden of isolation to reflect that a recent Miss Canada, in a Miss World contest, wore the cunningest little confection based on the Mountie uniform for her National Costumes appearance. Over her smooth little meringue of a face was a dear little Mountie hat, and then the briefest of little torso-tickling tunics, and a skirt ending mid thigh. And on television, too, in front of all those millions and millions of spectators. Some police forces get all the breaks, publicity-wise.

Well, no, she didn't actually win—but she made the semi-finals!

31

ONE OF THE crimes the Mounties did occasionally have to look into was hunting out of season, and the hunting of protected animals. The native deer, moose and elk had virtually disappeared, like the beaver, except in the National Parks. None the less they were hunted. A couple of our neighbours occasionally went on hunting trips after the harvest in the autumn. They went away to the west, somewhere near the foothills, I believe. As like as not the game they came back with was on the prohibited list, but they were somehow not among the men that the Mounties always caught.

Most of the hunting, though, was done by the children. We hunted crows and magpies, their eggs and the pairs of feet of the young ones being worth a small bounty from the municipality. We also hunted the gopher, whose depredations during the drought period (which seemed to favour their proliferation) became really burdensome to the farmer.

This sort of hunting was left to the children, being beneath the notice of adult males. Except for Mr Schmaltz. When he learned of the bounty on gopher tails (probably a penny for every tail or every two tails) his heart leapt up; gophers were his only prolific crop. His big blue eyes twinkled and his innocent glee stretched from ear to ear as he announced to all and sundry how he would let his gophers go, after pulling off the tail, until a new tail had grown which would make it worth his while to catch the animal again—and again and again. He was sure that this was going to be an improvement on work as a means of making a living.

Whether he actually did try to farm his gophers in this fashion, or just talked about it, I don't know, but his dedication to unwork certainly involved him in one bizarre scheme after another. He was a pushover for the pedlars of Eldorados, of gold or silver or copper mines, of diamond deposits. Whenever he did happen to lay hands on a dollar he always seemed to encounter, with near-miraculous promptness, a man who was selling something marvellously 'sheep' (he could not pronounce *ch*) in which he believed implicitly. No number of disappointments could destroy, or even dent, the unbelievable virginity of his Teutonic mind inside its large, round, flaxen-haired head. I can remember him actually rushing in on us once, in great excitement, having just bought a tropical island, lush with breadfruit trees and palms and bananas, and trying to coax my father to grubstake him. He had spent his last five dollars buying the title deed to the island—it was in the Caribbean, if I remember correctly—and if only he could get his fare and the world's most modest grubstake we would soon all be rich. In his mind he had already cornered the market in breadfruit and coconuts, and was doing a brisk trade in bananas as well.

Anything could be sold to Schmaltz, although where he got the cash at all to buy it with defeats me. He bought ancient farm machinery, cracked chamber-pots, broken bits of harness, the unsaleable lots left at the end of the sales of household goods in an unaffluent community. He was always going to mend, polish, reassemble and resell at an immense and deceptively simple profit. Of course nothing was ever mended or resold, and the junk spread out like lava from his house until it covered almost all of his fifth-rate quarter section: whatever else the land might have been good for was forgotten while Schmaltz pursued his schemes. If he did get around to some seeding, it was probably so late that even if there was enough rain to germinate the seed it had no chance to ripen before the big freeze came. His place was more or less habitable while his wife lived, but after the poor embattled creature died—young, of course—he produced a veritable show-place of a rural slum in a country where the phenomenon, although not common, was by no means unknown.

For a while after his wife died he had a way of turning up, about meal time, at one house or another in the neighbourhood, and was invariably invited to dine with the family. He usually had Heinzie with him—Heinzie would have been only eight or nine at the time. Nobody minded though. He radiated a splendid, blockheaded innocence, not without cunning—like the good soldier Schweik, who also managed to survive without too much conformity in difficult circumstances.

His amiability was utterly unshakable. I can remember him having dinner (the noon meal) with us when I was quite little, and my brothers still brats of boys, and Francis persuading him to shovel a great spoonful of freshly ground horse-radish into his mouth under the delusion that it was a new kind of ice-cream. Before the rusty telegraph centre of his mind could get any lines

33

cleared to dispatch warning signals he had already swallowed it, and as he bolted for the door you could all but see the steam rising out of the top of his head. Even now, more than thirty years later, Francis can still raise a chuckle out of the memory—country humour is nothing if not durable. But Schmaltz bore him no ill will. He thought it a good joke—on the wrong person maybe, but yes, a good joke.

He had one great treasure which did a lot to raise his stock with small boys, and even to diminish his absurdity in the eyes of their elders. It was the smashed-flat watch which had stopped what would otherwise have been a lethal bullet during the First World War. No one thought the worse of him for having fought on the 'wrong side' in that war, which was ancient and far-away history to most people. Even if there had been any current of anti-German sentiment I doubt if it would have occurred to anyone that Schmaltz might have been an asset and comfort to the foe.

Heinzie was of military age for the Second World War, and went into the army. He wrote to my mother from England, asking her to write to him. His mother was dead, his sister had already started her sad oscillation between the inside and the outside of mental hospitals, his father and his older brother were too indolent and indifferent to make any attempt to communicate with him, and he wanted to get letters from something he could think of as home. My mother was touched and pleased, and sent him her best weather and crop reports in her firm, flowing hand with faithful regularity, and a sort of affection grew up between them. But in London he met and married a walking slum, and after the war they came back and settled down alongside Schmaltz senior to a level of quite unbelievable soapless, beery shiftlessness. His ties with my mother petered out, although, to her credit, she was genuinely sorry when he landed in jail—a little matter of his having resorted to some activity other than work to make ends meet once the post-war credits had been guzzled. My mother was inclined to blame the wife. If he had married the right woman, she said, she might have made something out of Heinzie —not much, maybe, but something.

Germany can afford its economic miracle: Schmaltz and his heirs have emigrated for ever.

THEY CALLED his name Emmanuel—Emmanuel Morgan. He was born in Sheffield, England, about 1870. At the age of ten he descended into the coal mines, but did not rise again on the third day, nor even on the third year. He did, however, eventually rise again, although only so far as our home, which was considerably below the heavens. He became, I suppose, a member of our family, and lived with us for years and years. He lived in my father's house far longer than I did.

He was with us from my earliest memory. He never came into the living-room with us, when we all gathered there in the warm around the best stove in the house of a winter's evening. He would have been welcome there. The standing invitation was repeated from time to time, especially when the cold south-east wind made the kitchen nearly uninhabitable. Only occasion-ally, when we were still children young enough for our mother to read aloud to from some particularly thrilling book—*Call of the Wild*, or *Huckleberry Finn*—he would bring a straight-backed kitchen chair just inside the door and sit there, wary as a half-tamed animal, to hear the reading. As soon as it was finished he would retire again to his corner of the kitchen, where he sat on the old brown-covered boot box, sucking away at his pipe, the coal-oil lamplight hardly dispersing the cavernous shadows around him.

He had a quarter section of land a couple of miles away on which was a tiny one-roomed tarpaper shack. He had four large incredibly placid and slow horses—King, Prince, Duke and Fuzzy. He hitched them to his inadequate machinery and scratched tentatively at the surface of his farm, commuting to and from our house at a snail's pace. Left to his own devices he lived exclu-sively on bread and butter and tea and potatoes. At our table he ate fairly normally, but would reject anything which he had never tried during his childhood, and annually warned us in season that tomatoes had been considered very dodgy things to eat and were possibly even poisonous. I believe that he had at one time fallen so ill that he had had to be hospitalized (during which experience he had been subjected to baths, which had proved traumatic), had subsequently come to our house to convalesce, and had simply never left. His underworked horses loafed about in our pasture eating our overgrazed, dried-out grass. He helped

35

with the milking morning and night—but never more than a couple of cows, and those the easier and more docile ones— and did no other chores. On washdays he delivered up the clothes he had worn for the past week, but only under duress, letting it be known that all this washing and changing was not only un- necessary but unwholesome; instead of becoming more acquiescent with the passing of years in this matter he became more and more obdurate, and for some time refused to yield up the dirty clothes at all until my mother forbade him to sit down at the table until he had changed. He never took a bath, not even annually, a fact which was commented upon by such hired men or brothers as might have to share his bedroom, and there was no escape from sharing in our overcrowded house. He was hardly the ideal cell-mate during those broiling summer nights when not a breath stirred the curtains and the heat lightning, making the darkness visible, mocked us with dreams of cooling thunder showers. He paid nothing for board or bed—his farming methods would hardly produce enough, during those times, to keep him in tobacco and clothing—but he did insist upon planting a garden by his shack and growing vegetables of which he made a series of unsolicited and often unwanted gifts. He would arrive with boxes of peas, picked just a week too late when they were getting hard and tasteless, or turn up with bushels of string beans when we were already up to the eyeballs in string beans and offering them to the neighbours.

I accepted his presence in our family just as I accepted all other presences, human and animal. He was a part of That Which Was. He was very fond of little children. I have seen him playing with Alice's and Francis's babies, bouncing them wildly, their little heads lolling madly about as if ready to fall off and roll away at any moment, mothers biting their nails with apprehension and muttering the First Law of Infants: Support the head firmly at all times. The babies adored it and gurgled and laughed. The mothers survived.

It is probable that he bounced me about so. My earliest recollection of him is of his drawing his special beetle—the one with the buttons down the front of its waistcoat—on the blackboard which hung on the kitchen wall. As I started learning to read and write I was anxious that he should participate in this too, but this was the sad point at which he started gradually withdrawing from his intimacy with children, for he could do neither. I have seen him, with my father helping and encouraging, manage to scratch his name, Emmanuel Morgan, on some legal document, but the trembling and sweating and humiliation were painful to behold.

As I grew older I formed a distinct image of the inside of his mind. It was like a windowless attic into which anything and everything had been shoved through the trap-door. Through that trap-door, which was the only access, could come enough dim and indirect light to show that the attic was not empty—indeed it was quite stuffed—but not enough light really to illuminate anything. Only a few objects, those nearest to the trap-door, were even identifiable. But curiously enough I don't think I ever thought him stupid. None of us did, not even my mother when she was moved to extreme exasperation by some cantankerousness. More than any person I have ever known, he seemed quite simply to have been denied light.

We were very fond of his little, little fund of songs, anecdotes and stories as children. His songs were 'Soldiers of the Queen' and 'I Have Heard the May Bird Singing'. It did not seem odd that he never learned any others. He had those, treasured for their scarcity value. He had a couple of anecdotes from his mining days in Lethbridge, where he had worked for a while when he first came to Canada before he took up farming. Our favourite was of the man who had boasted how he would climb Cascade Mountain, at Banff, alone and unaided and in record time. The story invariably ended with the same punch line, delivered in a splendid thudding thumping North Country cadence: 'And they shovelled him up and put him in a sack.' He also talked sometimes of a period of soldiering in India. My principal recollection of the military discourses was the one on underwear. (One of his principal grievances was that my mother refused categorically to let him wear heavy woollen combination underwear during the summer. When we changed to summer cottons he had to change to summer cottons. She would not wash, nor require anyone else to wash, his heavy woollen underwear all summer long and That Was That.) In India, he recalled nostalgically, they had worn heavy woollen underwear all the time, day in and day out, year in and year out. They wore it *to keep the heat out*, and this protection was the only thing that enabled the English to stay in India. The Empire depended upon it. There was no other way to beat the climate.

He had one friend, an excessively solitary bachelor, Colin Smith. Colin's farm adjoined ours to the south. We usually saw him annually. Morgan was told to invite him to join us for Christmas and/or New Year's dinner, and he usually turned up for one of the other, affable and ill at ease, thankful for the chores which provided him with a good reason to leave early. Morgan used to go to him almost every Sunday, and a good many of his duels with my mother originated there. Colin used to spend most of Sunday reading the papers to Morgan, who returned to us retailing the news he had just learned. He often told us, as news, something of which he had been told several days earlier by my mother, or something which had been discussed already around our table in his presence. My mother would remind him that he had already known the item, to which he would reply, 'Colin seed it in the papers.' Colin was the only news source he recognized as unimpeachable, a fact which irked my mother more than somewhat over many, many years. She always prided herself on being authoritative. Even when we got radio and Morgan could hear the news on that, he didn't really believe it until Colin had verified it.

Besides Morgan's farm, his horses, his pipe and his friend was one other cherished possession, a large photograph in a heavy gilt frame of a little girl with a pretty, merry face and masses of ringlets, dressed in a solemn Sunday-best white dress with a pink ribbon sash. She was his daughter Ivy. I thought her enchanting, especially as my fine thin hair offered no hope of ever achieving ringlets for myself. He never spoke of her or of his family or of life in England, except to offer some piece of nutritional or hygienic or meteorological lore from his youth. He had presumably talked to my parents, however. They knew that he had come to Canada with the firm intention of sending for his wife and two children—for he had a son, Jimmy, also. He had worked hard in the mines in Lethbridge, and had saved up their passage money, and his mate Pat McGuffy had sent it off in a letter. He had gone to the bank and post office with Pat himself, and had seen it dispatched. I don't know whether he said that his wife had refused to join him, or that she had simply not turned up. It was only after he realized that they were never coming that he had left off mining and drifted up to our part of the world. He had of course lost contact with his family entirely.

I don't know when my mother started trying to trace them for him, nor whether the idea of doing so had been his or hers (hers, I would suspect), but I do know that she pursued one clue after another diligently over a period of years. She wrote to parish priests and town clerks and I know not who else. I think that it was just about the end of the Second World War when she finally caught up with them. His wife was dead, but his son and daughter were still very much alive, both married, both with children, and indeed his son was himself already a grandfather. They were thrilled to have made contact with their old father after so many years.

Old Morgan's reaction was curious. He refused point blank to have any part of them. He denied that they were his children. So there must have been another Emmanuel Morgan, miner, who emigrated to Canada from Sheffield twenty-odd years before, leaving behind one son James and one daughter Ivy. He couldn't account for the coincidence, but certainly there must have been one, for this lot were nothing to him.

Ivy and Jimmy filled in a few blanks for my mother. If any money for their passage had ever been sent their mother had most certainly never got it. After their father emigrated they had in fact received a few messages from him, penned by his obliging friend Pat—but no money. They had waited and waited, and after a while the messages simply stopped coming, and then their mother's letters had started being returned 'address unknown'.

I have only my mother's report of this matter, not having been around at the time myself. It seemed fairly obvious to her that Patrick McGuffy, Esq., had posted the passage money to himself. James and Ivy also accepted this probability—they seemed nice, stable citizens and refused to allow themselves to be put off by their father's withdrawal. Their mother must have been a splendid woman, for she had never fed any resentment of their lot or of their father's apparent desertion into them. They had

39

accepted his loss as due to the hazard of poverty and illiteracy, not to indifference or neglect. They understood, as my mother did not, that the old man might well be humiliated to be confronted with two persons who might reasonably have accused him of sneaking out on them when they most needed him. They kept writing, sent snapshots and little gifts, and bided their time. They could not possibly have done it in the hope of an inheritance, as it had been made clear from the beginning that Morgan had nothing to speak of.

My mother, as was her wont, was less delicate. She launched a full frontal attack. She bullied and badgered him into admitting finally that these were indeed his children, and into accepting that his friend Pat was probably a scoundrel. She said of Morgan, as if it were discreditable, that he was absolutely determined not to think badly of his trusted friend. She must (I think) have gone further and tried to make him see that he wasn't a good judge either of other men or of his own best interests, and that his habit of consulting with every Tom, Dick, Harry or Colin Smith was simply wrong-headed. It wouldn't be that she had anything against Colin Smith, just that it must be obvious, to all right-thinking persons, that she and my father were more suitable. She wouldn't have minded how much mere socializing he did with Colin; it was a question of recognizing the authoritative opinion.

My mother had then, I gather, proceeded to counsel him on the dispatching of passage money, undeterred by the fact that her counsel was a quarter of a century or so too late. He had had no business, she told him, entrusting it to a friend, another mere miner like himself. He ought to have taken it to the bank and asked to see the manager and got him to send the money. How a man like Morgan, whose entire life was covered with scar tissue from the usages privilege and power had practised upon his vulnerability from the beginning, ought to have known that you might never safely entrust small sums of money with persons who would treat your life's blood as a most casual, expendable asset, I do not know. But my mother felt that he ought to have known. She told him so. She told him that if only he had asked advice of sound people, instead of just anyone, he would have been made to see this. And, if I know my mother, she went on saying it, *ad nauseam*.

40

And something else came to light at this time. That period of military service in India: it was pure fantasy. She was thoroughly indignant about it, regarding it not as benign imagination diluting the bitterness of reality, but as outrage. She herself had small talent for the saving fantasy existence. I looked at him with a new respect. I had not thought that he had enough resources in him to scrape together even the little stock of simple credible tales which had possibly fooled him as much as they did us. It is a marvel to know that he had, however briefly, however modestly, partaken of imperial romance, and worn heavy woollen combinations day and night, year in and year out, in India. (Did the army ever wear woollen coms in India? It seems the sort of buttoned-up thing that just might go with the square-bashing, button-polishing side of imperialism.)

There was a limit to the size to which Emmanuel Morgan, illiterate one-time miner, would allow himself to be cut down. He packed up his pipe and his woollen underwear and left, taking up residence once more in his tiny shack, and he never came back to live in our house. But the row remained a family row: he was still included in our family gatherings and celebrations, being collected by Alice and Harry or by Francis, and brought along. His grocery list was called for and his groceries delivered to his shack. There was no ill-will, really, between him and my mother: they recognized each other as fundamentally well meaning, if mistaken. And through my mother, and with increasing enthusiasm, he communicated with his children. They wanted him to come back and let them care for him during his declining years.

I have visited them, in Sheffield, in Ivy's home; there is no doubt at all in my mind that their generous desire to accept and cherish their old, inadequate father was completely genuine and unforced. He wouldn't go back, of course. It was too far in distance and in time. He had for too many years accepted our family as his own to substitute another. His place amongst us might not always be comfortable or in line with his tastes, but it was familiar and undisputed. He had his rights and exercised them.

I saw him in 1960, the year before he died. By then he had had to give way and go into the old people's home—a brisk, hygienic, efficiently run institution—and submit himself to the indignity of baths, frequent changes of linen and the dominion of women. Obviously he didn't like it. He sat in his wheel-chair, unable to walk any more, and wept the humiliating and irrepressible tears of the old and helpless. Yet it was not too bad, and he knew it. He was pleased to see me, and asked about his son and daughter, knowing that I had seen them. He took an obvious pleasure in my account of them.

As for him, he still had his pipe—even if there were now some regulations attached to it. He had plenty of visitors, not only from my own family but from neighbours—anyone who happened to be in Mafeking with a few minutes to spare would drop in. There are worse places to sit, waiting for death.

THE GENUINE dirt farmer lives by chance. He is too familiar with chance to fool about with it or play games with it. So it was probably not typical of our neighbourhood to have even one gambler in it. But had there been any rigorous test to pass, I doubt if Walt Krohlsinger would have qualified, technically, as a dirt farmer.

As a gambler he had some success—quite enough to irritate those who like their social deviates to come to exemplary Bad Ends. He himself was close-mouthed about it, but his wife caused some consternation in the Ladies' Aid by announcing not only that she did not object to his cards, but also that she found them profitable, as he passed on some of his winnings when he was in a good mood. The stakes must have been fairly substantial, given the epoch and circumstances. Players were attracted from a considerable distance away, and one game might continue non-stop anything from forty-eight hours to a week. Players dropped in and players dropped out, but it was claimed that

Mother as a young lady in Iowa

Walt stayed until the game was over. There were pallets in the back room of the Chinese restaurant on which to snatch a brief snooze, there was an inexhaustible supply of sandwiches and coffee, and there was privacy.

Whoever benefited from the poker games, it was not the Krohlsinger kids. There were three of them: Eileen, Warren and Maynard. They all had crisply curling hair of genuine raven's-wing black with blue lights. They all had most beautiful violet blue eyes with long, sooty, curling lashes under faultlessly arched brows. They got their good features from their old man—and a good thing too: a man ought to give his children something.

Eileen and Maynard suffered considerably less than Warren, who was the elder son. The first two or three years Warren attended school his teachers gave up trying to keep him awake for lessons. At the advanced age of six years he was already up at five every morning, winter or summer, milking cows, carrying heavy buckets of pig feed and slops and water, pitching hay down to the work-horses, cleaning stables, and anything else Walt saw fit to unload on to his skinny shoulders. Fortunately for him, at seed time, haying season and harvest time Walt couldn't rouse enough players to keep a game going, and so only the relatively impossible rather than the absolutely impossible was demanded of him. And fortunately the law would not allow him to be kept home from school for more than a minimal period each school year. Otherwise his life would probably have been little easier than for old Morgan in the Sheffield collieries forty-five years and a mass of legislation earlier. The penalty for Warren's infant inadequacies in the performance of chores was a beating. Being a lad of considerable intelligence, little of which he squandered on formal education, he learned at an early age to pass his pain and humiliation on to others with truly remarkable success—of which more later—and himself maintained an air of jaunty insouciance.

You'd have thought Bessie Krohlsinger might have done something to make life easier for her fledglings. She was a good-natured enough woman and seemed to like her children. She was not without education, and I have heard that she had once taught school in Oregon or Washington State, although this always seemed a little difficult to believe. True, there was reading matter in their house—quite an extraordinary quantity of it. Walt read the pulpiest of pulp magazines about cowboys and train robbers and, especially, espionage in Washington, D.C. He did not differentiate between these fictions and journalism, and was bug-eyed with it all. Because he got a new spy-sex-and-violence story-book every week he actually thought that a new set of authentic scandals had been unearthed every week. He thought it nothing short of miraculous that they got any serious business of governing done at all in Washington with all those goings-on. He thought it scandalous. He was prim about it. Bessie preserved all Walt's 'books', and all the comics and weekly farm newspapers and wrapping paper and string and broken crockery and saucepans with holes, so far as one could see. She must have been a compulsive hoarder, and hoarding seemed to be only one amongst her compulsions.

Only some sort of compulsion could account for her attitude toward money, its getting and spending. For instance, she boasted that her children could not drink milk (even though they were milking the cows themselves) because *all the milk was needed for the pigs.* Even a moment's thought would have convinced anyone who wasn't cut on the bias that the audience of neighbourhood mothers to whom she delivered that observation was not going to think better of her for it. If there were others who put the pigs before their children they kept absolutely quiet about it. Not Bessie. Yet she was generous enough in contributing of her work and culinary achievements when there was an Aid sale or some other community activity. In fact she was modestly celebrated for her fancy cooking. But my brother Francis, who helped them with their haying a couple of summers, confirmed with sorrow the common rumour that when the party was over and they were back on everyday fare there was literally never enough to eat. There could have been no rational excuse for this. Even during the worst of the drought, gardens in our part of the country were always adequate, and vegetables were at their best about haying time. There would have been no advantage in skimping them to see the produce saved, for there was no sale for it thereabouts, and anyhow it would have been shocking to take money for vegetables from neighbours—like expecting them to pay for their bed if they spent the night. And even if meat was short—fresh meat was always a problem during the hot weather—the hens were always laying well during the summer. The Krohlsingers could have gone hungry only because Bessie required it of them—why, I cannot imagine. She herself looked as if she had never eaten a square meal in her life. Outside the photographs of concentration camp inmates I have never seen any ambulatory human being who was skinnier. With her halo of fuzzy, half-kempt hair, her acute angles and cackling laugh she was our first candidate for the pointed hat and broomstick.

What did she do with the money from Walt's winnings, the money from those milk-fed pigs and those eggs they hungered after in vain? Well, she didn't spent it on the house. I can't remember the house in detail, but I have a powerful impression of smallness (and the houses which I thought imposing in those days look like rabbit hatches to me now), of the clutter of paper and general junk, of the absence of a home-making feminine touch. The curtains were such as a man might have put up in a fit of absent-mindedness and then forgotten. There were no bedspreads, no gay, home-made quilts on the beds, just coarse grey blankets; there were no rugs on the linoleum beside the beds for bare feet to grope for on a winter's morning, not even home-sewn or crocheted from rugs. It was not that Bessie was lazy: she was known to be a hustler. But she spent her energies where there was a chance of a cash return, looking after livestock and poultry.

At the very nadir of the Depression, when the good times seemed so remote as to have passed quite beyond hope, when everyone seemed destined to pinch and scrape and do without for ever, Bessie turned up at the Ladies' Aid in a brand new muskrat coat for which she announced that she had paid fifty dollars. Fifty dollars was probably considerably more than our family of two adults and six children was then spending annually for clothing. (I should say at once that the Krohlsinger children were always dressed adequately by our standards, but thriftily, like the rest of us.) I can remember my mother shaking her head about that coat. Significantly, though, it did not excite nearly the indignation or irritation that Sigrid Varma's mere dyed rabbit—price unknown, but much cheaper—had done. Sigrid spent so much on her house and clothing and pushing Jake into buying a closed-in Plymouth sedan to replace the Model T Ford that Jake was never able to finish paying for the farm, and had to go on renting until he finally lost it completely. Sigrid demanded, and managed to extort, real status from her consumer habits, consequently she could hardly have bought a new dishmop without giving maximum offence. But Bessie Krohlsinger's fifty-dollar coat, like many other things about her, poised at the intersection of joke, mystery and exasperation. It was not an affront to anyone or anything except to rational intelligence—which is, of course, regularly affronted with impunity anywhere and everywhere.

It couldn't have been that Bessie thought she would look nice in that coat. The only thing she would really have looked nice in was an extra twenty pounds of solid flesh. Even *she* must have known that. Anyhow, she didn't really bother to comb her hair properly—not to get all the tangles out at the back, for instance, when she modelled the coat. It couldn't have been just to keep her warm, although there is a good case for a fur coat in that climate, and especially then, with transportation so slow and uncertain. But she wouldn't be wearing the coat when she was most exposed to the elements, at her chores around the farm. And again, an extra twenty pounds of flesh and a cloth coat would probably have been cosier than somebody else's skins. But there was one thing: the coat *did* make her happy.

Whatever judgment the outsider might have passed on Bessie, her children did not judge her too harshly. As soon as they were fifteen and could legally quit school, Warren and Eileen left home to fend for themselves. But they came back to see her regularly, and after Eileen married she used to have her mother with her for protracted visits. Maynard stayed on at home and took over the farm—but on his own terms. I believe that he demanded ownership early on, and managed to prise it out of the old man. (Walt wasn't all that old, but his sons always referred to him as 'the old man', and he sticks in the mind so.) Life on the farm was apparently tranquil enough for some years, Maynard running the place, Walt coming and going at will, but effectively excluded from management.

Then Bessie died. Maynard drove his father to the funeral.

When it was over he drove him back home, stood over him to supervise the bundling of some clothes into a suitcase, drove him to the station, bought him a one-way ticket to Edmonton, saw him on to the train, and told him not to come back—that he, Maynard, had had a bellyful. All this without fuss, it is said, but with finality.

The loss to the neighbourhood was sustained with equanimity.

I DON'T THINK our neighbourhood could claim to have been sexually dashing.

Even if the rigours of farming and child care had left any time and energy and appetite for sexual adventure amongst the more mature, the peculiar lack of privacy both in the home and in society—and the consequent suspicion of anyone who seeks privacy or follows any solitary interests—would have made discreet liaison almost impossible.

It is true that there were few non-essential weddings during the Depression period, which is the time when my own memory started tucking away information, and that there were none the less quite a lot of weddings, and that numerous citizens expressed themselves scandalized thereby. But the belated wedding was a world-wide phenomenon, I believe, during those dreary times. Youth has ever been awkward about agreeing to impotence, even for the most solemn reasons. . . .

I suppose that the career of Thea was just about our Alpha and Omega of satisfactory fruity sexual scandal. Strictly speaking, she lived outside our community, but she did turn up at our schoolhouse dances sometimes where, it was said, she turned an honest dollar. Being too young at the time to attend these dances myself I cannot say with certainty whether she was a brisk professional or an obliging occasional amateur. But pro or amateur, she and her clients would have needed aplomb, to say the least. The dances were after all very small gatherings—probably twenty-five to forty persons in all—and all neighbours, without any hope of anonymity whatsoever. They were assembled in one small room with only one exit, and that one (as I observed in later years when I went to dances myself) would have been inevitably and permanently blocked by a gangle of gawking, gossiping, giggling stags who would have eased their own awkwardness by loudly clocking the couple in and out, by laying bets on male prowess (on whether the man would rank higher for speed of dispatch or for the length of time he could monopolize her attention in return for the fee). In any event, Thea's exits and entrances with—or without—her partners must have been heralded with something like trumpet voluntaries.

I saw Thea only once that I can recall, and thought her most attractive. She was brunette and plump and lively and, to my young eyes—I would have been ten, perhaps, or eleven at the time—she appeared neither sinful nor *fatale*. So far as I know she was treated with civility, although it may have been a somewhat reluctant civility, even by those respectable matrons who disapproved most. I believe that she eventually married a local farmer and settled down to a life too unspectacular to provide any sort of satisfactory cautionary Bad End.

Yrdis Olafson was a different matter. There was certainly some laughter at her expense—but then I have heard men convulsed with laughter by the antics of Blanche Dubois, apparently under the impression that *Streetcar Named Desire* is a protracted and hilarious dirty joke. But most people, although they had heard about Yrdis, pretended not to have heard. She made them uneasy. She was not ostracized by the Ladies' Aid.

One can be reasonably certain that, whatever sympathy the other ladies might have felt for her husband, none coveted him. It is unlikely that Clarence Olafson could be technically certified as either idiot or imbecile, but certainly he needed a considerable mull at some such announcement as 'It looks a little like rain', to get the hang of it. I had no dealings with Clarence myself, but his eldest boy, who was his carbon copy, went to school with me. When the news was passed on to him that two and two make four his sustained astonishment was memorable.

Yrdis and Clarence Olafson had six children, born in the first eight or nine years of their marriage. When, for reasons unknown to me, Yrdis ceased child-bearing, she already had a look of comfortable and respectable middle age, although she must have been closer to twenty-five than thirty. Her children were always scrubbed clean, their faces radiated health, their clothes were beautifully laundered and mended, and their school lunches always up to the best of the modest standards to which we aspired. There can be no doubt that Yrdis loved and slaved for her children.

Nevertheless there were occasions. Their tale presumably lost nothing during the journey to my ears, nor, in all probability, has my memory diminished them. But, allowing for all this, there were certainly occasions when Yrdis dolled herself up and walked out, leaving Clarence to sort out the family. She would walk or hitch-hike to a dance somewhere and, if events were satisfactory, would leave that dance with some man and would not return to her family until Clarence came and got her. In order to do this Clarence would have to hitch his team to the wagon and go hang-dogging around the neighbours first, to get a line on where she might be found. And then she might keep him waiting, throwing taunts at him from another man's door, shouting that she hadn't had enough yet, that he should come back tomorrow or next Tuesday and see if she could stand the sight of him by then. Or she might contrive to keep him prowling around outside some public place, pitiful in his impotent rage and dependence upon her. And the little children waiting for them at home.

I am under the impression that the local men shied away from Yrdis's charms, whether through decency or fear or mere discretion. She tended to couple with men outside our usual orbit.

Clarence was said to give her a good beating sometimes when he finally *did* get her home, but it is unlikely that mere physical pain could have made much impression, or would have afforded them or even the neighbours much gratification.

For Yrdis had been born a Thorsen and, as if that wasn't enough, she had been the eldest one.

I was perhaps eleven when Mrs Thorsen and the nine or ten

children who were still young enough to be in her care moved into the district. Yrdis was already married then, and her eldest boy must have started school that year or the next, along with a selection of the Thorsen girls—his aunts.

I don't know where the Thorsens came from—not far away, I dare say. They moved into a tiny, rotting, abandoned, sod-roofed, one-room, homesteader's log shack. Whether they had prior permission from the farmer on whose land the shack stood I don't know, but he must have been a generous man, for they could not possibly have paid him anything, and he allowed them to take a little plot for a vegetable garden, and to run a few chickens and a cow. Without that they must have starved or been reduced to unimaginable poverty.

The ratepayers—or perhaps one should say the rate defaulters —looked at first with stony eyes on this obviously indigent brood, but the women soon softened to Mrs Thorsen, who was obviously hard-working and trying desperately to be a good mother in such appalling circumstances. When the first winter clamped down after their arrival in our midst, the Thorsen children dropped out of school, and the authorities soon discovered that they had no shoes or warm clothing. They got some relief, and quite a lot of dismal but still wearable leftovers from the rest of us, and settled down to survive in our midst. The women were soon arranging that, whenever possible, Mrs Thorsen should be offered rides to the Ladies' Aid meetings— which was no small item, as her three or four or five pre-school-age children would have to be included. She did not make it regularly at all, but did sometimes. I saw her seldom, and would perhaps have forgotten or simply not noticed her had I not been involved in her children's hell at school. She was a drably clothed, shapeless mass of a woman, fat with the fat of perpetual pregnancy and a diet which was mostly potatoes. She sat at Ladies' Aid meetings in a state which looked to be but little short of beatitude, too happy to be of society to wish to use it for any purpose. I don't mean that she was humble: she was treated, and carried herself, as equal to the others. She even once volunteered her home for a meeting, and the meeting was held there with Mrs Thorsen providing refreshments and being the hostess, and no one would have dreamed of refusing her offer or of criticizing the appointments. But just to be there, to hear the other women talking, was enough: she did not need to talk herself, not even to second a motion.

I think that it must have been in connection with Mr Thorsen that I heard my father speak of the possibility that his wages might be 'garnisheed' by the municipal authorities and spent on the care of his family. I remember that word, for it struck me instantly as being a glamorous word, and I obstinately refused to recognize its dreary associations. (Like a friend of mine who, hearing her father speak of the latrines of Paris, after the First World War, named her dolly Latrine because it was such a lovely, feminine word.) Mr Thorsen was a coal-miner and plied his trade in a small hole in the ground some twenty or thirty miles away which supplied coal to the locals. It is unlikely that he made much money. He was reputed to be a hard worker—which rated so highly among the virtues that people were being perpetually astonished to find how many vices could accompany industry. I believe that Mr Thorsen was also accused of being a drinking man.

Be that as it may, there were few in our parts who had so much as set eyes on him. He turned up regularly, however. His was a spring rutting season. He turned up for two or three weeks every spring, exercised his conjugal rights, which he could not seem to do to his satisfaction without beating his wife viciously— and I do not mean just the occasional cheerful black eye: I have myself seen her face still misshapen and marbled with scars and fading bruises, and heaven only knows what infamies were concealed by her clothing—in the presence of his terrorized and helpless children, then vanished for another year, leaving them to face the swelling belly and subsequent miracle of birth in utter destitution.

As Thorsen never, to my knowledge, attended any public function in the neighbourhood, there was never any public demonstration of the communal opinion of him—not that it would have amounted to much, I think. My mother's indignation and revulsion would have been pretty general amongst the women, I suspect, and they would probably have avoided speaking to him without cutting him ostentatiously. The men would probably have treated him with the cautious civility which the ladies reserved for Thea. It was a serious and unusual thing for an able-bodied man to allow his family to become something of a charge on the community. As for the wife-beating, well, nobody else indulged in it that I ever heard of in those parts.

As to what the Thorsens themselves made of it, there is Yrdis, married at the age of fifteen or sixteen presumably to the first man who offered—anything, anyone to escape. Or was Clarence just anyone? Was he even the first offer? (She must have been quite an attractive young girl.) Would she, had she waited another decade and played the whole field, have found another victim so vulnerable, a man on whom one could vent the venom of an utterly poisoned childhood, one who could be despised publicly, with impunity?

The eldest Thorsen boy just got out and stayed out. Odvar, the second boy, had turned into a strapping young man of nineteen or twenty some five years after the family settled amongst us, and whether by chance or design was home on a visit himself one spring when his honoured father turned up. I guess that Odvar beat him into something that looked about as minced and dazed as Mrs Thorsen usually did after the conjugal bit, and promised to kill him if he turned up again, which he was wise enough not to do.

But the uneventful years remaining to Mrs Thorsen were few. She died, not yet forty years old, in hospital and in receipt of decent medical attention, but it was said that the doctors were puzzled to name the specific cause of death. It seems that her heart, kidneys, liver, gall bladder, blood circulation and practically every other item in her physiological catalogue were so exhausted and malfunctioning that it was almost impossible to know which had delivered the *coup de grâce*.

WE PRODUCED, as a community, plenty of gossip and
grumbling and disapproval. No one approved of
Thorsen's ugly brutality or the neglect of his children, but no one did anything about it. I believe that the talk of
garnisheeing his wages was dropped almost as soon as it was
broached, as it seemed unlikely that his small and intermittent
income was worth pursuit. No one approved of Yrdis's hysterical
adventures, or of Walt Krohlsinger's exploitation of his infant
labour force to the point of exhaustion, nor of their being
undernourished, but no one would have dreamed of interfering
or of ostracizing the parents. No phalanx of righteous matrons
stepped forth to forbid Thea's entrance to our social occasions.
A secular, tolerant society, one to be excited to solemn public
action by nothing short of murder itself, one might think. And
yet I did so.

I have never been a great hand for exact chronology, but as
nearly as I can work it out I believe that I must have been twelve
at the time. It is not irrelevant. The newspaper report of someone hit by a car on the road will invariably start, 'Thirty-one
year old mother of two. . . .' How much more important are the
vital statistics of the individual who rocks the social boat to the
point at which panic stations are sounded and all hands must
leap to man the pumps to prevent imminent capsize.

Both Francis and Wilbur were still going to school during my
first two years there, and Wilbur still during my third year, so I
must have been about eight or nine before my role as Warren
Krohlsinger's number one victim was assumed, this being the
sort of role which does not fall to citizens with big brothers at
hand. Warren was a born leader—my suspicions of the breed
have remained ever since—who managed to establish his
dominion over the entire school even before he was The Big
Boy, so that to be his victim meant that one had no friends or
allies whatsoever. As there is no dearth of memoirs and literary
guides to the cruelties of school children I shall not much
elaborate on my life and times under the administration of
Warren Krohlsinger, which differed only in detail, not in
essence, from other lives and times under other sadistic school-
boy administrations. I would mention, though, that the punish-
ments invented by him and his lieutenants were not physical.

53

I believe that I was actually beaten only once, and that not drastically. My recollection of my compensatory fantasy life of those days is actually sharper than memories of the persecutions and is probably a sufficient guide to them. In my dreams I was a softball star (softball was our junior, less dangerous variant of baseball) graciously allowing my persecutors to play short-stop or first base to my pitcher; or I was a ski champion, or a tamer of wild horses, of which I had the champion Vista-Vision stallion who would allow none but me to ride him. I was, in short, everything except a scrawny little girl who was hopeless at sports, inevitably the last person chosen for any team. I was good enough at school work, but that was hardly calculated to raise my stock with the other children—although I doubt if they resented it, being too indifferent to education to notice it much. I suffered agonies of embarrassment from a recurrent and unsightly dermatitis on my hands which I, along with my tormentors, assumed was associated with our rather substandard hygiene. I used to scrub and scrub my hands, and did not learn, until I was nearly twenty and suffered such an extreme attack that I consulted a skin specialist, that I was simply allergic to a host of things, among which was the excessive use of soap which I had used to try to be rid of it. We did not, during my childhood, bother doctors with mere trifles like 'the itch'.

When Warren graduated from being merely the dominant boy to being dominant *and* The Big Boy as well he extended his influence beyond merely tormenting me. The school had never been particularly remarkable. It was not large. In my time there would only have been fifteen to twenty pupils, spread over eight or nine grades. But teachers found it increasingly difficult to maintain control. The school board changed teachers every year, looking always for that more experienced—or larger or squarer or more compact—teacher who was going to settle our hash for us once for all. When I was in Grade VI someone hit on the obvious solution: what we needed was A Man's Hand. So we had our first man teacher. He had curly hair and I was madly in love with him. But he was not, alas, a disciplinarian. He disappeared about Christmas time with what was called 'nervous breakdown'. I believe that he never returned to teaching, and many years later my mother sent me a newspaper report of his death. He had been farming then for twenty-five years or so, was married and had five children, all of them quite young. His wife had, it seems, slipped off to a neighbour's and telephoned the doctor, who had recently released him from the mental hospital in which he had been treated for another of his 'nervous breakdowns', to say that she was frightened, and thought he had been released too soon. The doctor had made soothing professional noises at her and prevailed upon her to try a little harder a little longer. The next visitor to their farm found that my Grade VI teacher had taken his double-barrelled shotgun and shot his wife, his five children, the hired man and finally himself. There was blood and confusion everywhere. He would have had to load his gun at least four times.

But to return to Grade VI: between that Christmas and the end of the school year—about the third week in June—we went through not one, not two, but *three* teachers. And this at a time when jobs were so scarce and teachers so plentiful that resignation would have been an act of despair. That was the year in which the visiting Inspector of Schools declared flatly, in our presence, that we were the worst school in his entire district (which I would venture to guess contained a hundred schools or more) and that, moreover, he believed that we might well be the worst school he had ever had the misfortune to visit. Even I, the nearest thing to a scholar which the school then possessed, walked a little taller for sharing in the corporate distinction, and Warren was almost gracious—he was so satisfied—for a little time thereafter.

Indeed curiously enough that year did not seem quite so bad as the years which enclosed it. Not that I personally could have won any popularity contests, but the active concentrated persecution was directed toward other, non-child, targets. Most of its energies went into pure indiscipline, into genuine anti-authority. I had nothing against any of our teachers, and indeed liked some of them, but I felt that they could look after themselves. I even experienced, briefly and infrequently, some communal approval for my part in some anti-authority campaign.

Whether our rebellion just petered out, or whether Miss Rayne from Mafeking who came the following year—specially recommended to the school board by the Inspector of Schools

himself, for her experience of problem schools—really did have
sufficient authority to prevail over us, I couldn't say. We didn't
run her out, and something approximating order returned to
the school. But little of the old persecution returned to fall
upon my head because that year, God help them, the Thorsen
children had moved into our school district. There must have
been four of them who turned up for classes that autumn;
Gerda, Ingeborg, Marie and Helen. They were wretchedly
clothed, mousy and either puffy or wizened. Because, I suppose, of
their haphazard diet and lack of sanitation they all had abominable
breath and body odour. Warren, ever witty, christened them
The Reekies at once. I don't suppose they could afford soap.
Few of the children in the school were paragons of cleanliness,
but none of the others had those grey layers of undisturbed
grime, the scaly scalps, which encrusted the Thorsens; and
Warren, although not naturally fastidious himself, could not
bear to let the grime, any more than the odours, pass without
continuous comment. They tried, poor devils, to creep off by
themselves to eat their lunches—especially when their lunch-
buckets held nothing but little potatoes, cold, boiled in their
jackets (and, in midwinter, frozen on the way to school as well).
But Warren would manage to be there, with his attendant
sycophants, to make sure that no one missed the spectacle of the
opening of the only lunch-buckets without bread. Sometimes, as
a special treat to his expectant audience, he would have arranged
some little surprise—a horse turd or two in amongst the potatoes,
or some similar knee-slapper. It was not possible to avoid these
entertainments. As an article of faith, apparently, teachers
dispatched us outside to 'play' at recesses and noons; I believe
the idea was that we must not be deprived of fresh air and
exercise unless the weather was very inclement indeed. As
only two children in the whole school lived less than a mile
from the school, however, and as most lived two to three miles
away and had to carry wood and water, gather eggs, bring in
cows, or other wholesome country pursuits after they got home,
this all seemed pretty gratuitous to me. I would have given—I
know not what, but a lot—just to have been allowed to sit
quietly reading at my desk, having been a bookworm from times
before I could even read. But no. The Thorsens could not stay

in where it was safe, and I, being put out, must go and watch them be tormented, for Warren took an exceedingly dim view of those who shirked attendance at his entertainments.

Although I could not suppress a feeling of relief that the persecution had passed away from me, no more could I suppress the shameful awareness that I owed my salvation to the unrelenting torment of the Thorsens, whose life, outside school, offered far fewer compensations that my own. (Amongst my pet dislikes are people who piously observe, of some unfortunate, that 'There, but for the grace of God, go I'—as if there is anything gracious about a god simply because the creature he has selected for torment is not oneself.) I would have liked to help the Thorsens, but I was neither wise nor brave enough. The best I could manage was just to contribute nothing towards their persecution myself.

But the old imperious desire to be not merely tolerated, but liked and admired, as I was in my daydreams, asserted itself. Lousy as our little school community was, and as I knew it to be, it was the only world I knew outside my not very cosy family circle. My need for acceptance and intimacy preceded my schoolfellows and their particular individual characteristics, and blandly pushed me into ignoring their known unsuitability. I set out to woo. As I said, I think I must have been twelve then.

The person who had to be won, if I were to belong, was Warren. There was no other key to membership: no one else counted. Few alternatives suggested themselves in the matter of ingratiating oneself with Warren. The obvious one—Thorsen-baiting—was out. I don't know how I stumbled upon the other, subterranean one. But I did.

I discovered the uses of salaciousness. I found that I could, at the drop of a hat, turn out doggerel parodies of songs and poems utilizing our complete supply of four-letter words. (I believe that this part of my vocabulary has been complete since I was nine or ten, since when all that I have added have been those long latinate words which mean the same thing but look and sound safely gelded.) There followed a period, golden, brief and fruitless as an Indian summer, when I was the most sought-after child in the school. I monopolized the reading public and, for the first and only time in all my time in that school, the entire public

57

seemed to want to read. Wherever I chose to disport myself at recess or noon hour, whether behind the coal shed or in the barn or at the swings, so that the ear of authority be not at hand, there was the entire school applauding my every *bon mot*. For a little while even the Thorsens went unharassed, and could hover wistfully on the fringes of social existence. I must have turned out a near record quantity of infant obscenities, which I read out from carefully guarded scraps of grimy paper. I even wrote a parody of one of the songs we were learning for the spring music festival in Mafeking, which recorded the hypothetical sexual adventures of Miss Rayne and the young man who was currently her escort to dances, movies and picnics. Warren was so impressed by this one that he did me the signal honour of asking to borrow it long enough to make a copy. I let him borrow it.

The next morning, when I came to school, the sky had fallen. No one crowded around. No one spoke to me or came near— but no one took his eyes off me for an instant either.

At recess, however, Warren himself briefed me. He was in a state of manic excitement, totally and typically devoid of remorse. The previous day he had found a moment, when school was dismissed and when Miss Rayne's back was turned, to deposit my *opus* with its tale of her sexual life on her desk. It was of course in my own handwriting, familiar to her. Subsequently he reported, with the detached gratification of a scientist whose experiments are turning out well, she had arrived on foot, hysterical and incoherent, at Lars Olafson's place. (Lars was a distant relation to Clarence, but more 'there'. He had three children going to school at that time, of whom two were amongst Warren's most zealous disciples.) The Olafsons had calmed her down, and the adults then took counsel over my grubby piece of paper, after which east and west and south and north the messengers rode fast. Warren assured me that the entire school board, supported by other interested citizens, would be coming to have words with and about me that very afternoon.

I was too sick to feel anything else—not even anger towards Warren. Anger would in any event have been inappropriate. Warren was simply being true to his nature, and his nature had never exactly been kept secret from me. One might as well have criticized the lark for singing.

58

My memory of the following hours is feverish—vivid but distorted, with many gaps. There were the other children— my insatiably eager auditors of yesterday. Those Greek choruses were no mere poetic or theatrical convention. Fishy-eyed, weighed pear-shaped by fatalism, wired for cheerless noises, they must have camped or prowled unsleeping at the gates, lifting their muzzles to sniff and howl over the scent of trouble as if it were so much carrion. The chorus knew all along—uncon- sciously, perhaps, but it knew—who Oedipus really was. That's how they all managed to be there, on cue, equipped with sandwiches and flasks of coffee and brandy and opera glasses. I accepted, of course, the unspoken premiss of my own little chorus that I, having been caught, was mysteriously and horribly guilty, and that they, although equally initiated into the forbidden mysteries of sex, obscenity and the slander of school-teachers, were not guilty of anything and not to be involved. I could quite understand the care they took not to touch me physically.

I can remember Miss Rayne too, pale but composed. I could visualize her hysterical distress of the previous day which seemed to me, considering the enormity of my crime, to have been an appropriate reaction. I liked her rather than not, and was genuinely sorry to have done her this injury. There had never been any intent, after all, to injure her.

Somehow the hours passed, and the afternoon, and with it my inquisitors, arrived. And my parents. I could not have believed that their mere presence could be such a horror. I did not for one moment question the justice of these adults sitting in judgment and passing sentence upon me. It seems highly improbable to me now that there was amongst them one citizen who had not known, and found uses for, the lore and vocabulary of sexuality when he was twelve years old, but this thought most certainly never crossed my mind then. I felt that I, and none other, was steeped in the most criminal obscenity, and I wanted to die.

Whether my trial was long or short I don't know. It seemed of course interminable. I have no idea whether Miss Rayne found it curious or not, but as I recall it she might well have done. Ostensibly they were there to redress the injury done to her, but although they all read my masterpiece, passing its grubby and unsymmetrical inconsequence from hand to solemn hand

E

(for many, surely, the first—and probably the last—verse they had focused their eyes on since leaving school decades before), they were cursory in their attitude towards the wrong done to her. I doubt if they had plotted amongst themselves in advance, or had even figured out individually, what they might work with this bit of paper, but it was soon apparent that Miss Rayne would have to make do with their perfunctory acceptance of my statement that I did not believe the allegations to be actually true, as written down, and that I was sorry to have written them.

Where had I learned those words?

I didn't know. Pressed, I supposed that I had heard them at school (I still suppose so). Pressed further, I could add nothing. They interrogated me at length about this. They insisted on knowing when, where and from whom I had first heard these words, and took my inability to supply this information for stubbornness or deceit or insolence. (Where and when and from whom had *they* first learned these words? Not one of them required a glossary to read my text. . . .) But I did not question then the validity of this line of questioning, although in truth I can think of almost no word of which I could say that I first heard it on Tuesday, 15th March 1934, during the course of a conversation overheard between Mr Varma and Mrs Dawson. I don't know where I picked up 'onomatopoeia', or 'bicycle', or anything. Most words must drop into the mind and lie there dormant as the Sleeping Beauty until something happens to make the child attach meaning to their sound.

My judges went on interminably. Never was love letter picked so threadbare of meaning and implication as my poor, puerile, smutty doggerel by those solemn elders. Never did an apprentice Ph.D. extract more matter from so modest a text to please his examiners. I did not know then that their reaction to the stimulus of my text was morbidly excessive.

I forgot about it, more or less, years ago—better things to think about. And then, nearly thirty years later in London, half a world away, it all came back to me. On the lawns before my block of flats I moved amongst the unwontedly animated and communicative groups of housewives and young mothers keeping a weather eye on their toddlers, all out enjoying an afternoon of precious, unseasonable, early spring sunshine.

Half way through the afternoon—long before the tea time which would normally have depopulated the green—the little assemblies melted away, although the sun was still warm and inviting. I knew that all over Britain the same phenomenon was occurring, that only the most urgent business would keep people from their television sets. The House of Commons was opening its debate on the Profumo affair. For the first time since Edward was Prince of Wales a public figure was present, by name, in the 'dirty' jokes of at least two continents. A folk hero was born. A cold coming he must have had of it too, for all the unseasonable sunshine in the air.

For all my remembrance of being, myself, the prisoner in the dock, I too was soon glued to my television set, as greedy-eyed, beady-eyed and ambivalent as the rest. Even the ranks of Dimbleby could scarce forbear to leer.

My own little world which disintegrated on that other spring day of judgment was miniscule, shabby, unimportant. Yet it was the only world I knew then—all I had. There was no escape from it yet, either; for another two years I would have to live out every day of my life in the presence of those who had accomplished or witnessed my public humiliation. (I think I did not even forgive my parents for witnessing it. Not that they had wanted to do so, or had been anything but loyal to me during the proceedings, which must have unbelievably distasteful to them.) There was a time during the inquest when indeed my inquisitors tried to involve my parents in my disgrace by association, attempting to establish that depravity, like charity, must begin at home. The insinuation that I had learned my vocabulary from my parents and carried it to school to infect my innocent little playmates (how all their little haloes glowed, and gave off a gentle heat!) was the only thing which roused me from my pallid, monosyllabic hopelessness. But it was small wonder, a short time after this when my father was called to account for 'short-changing' Miss Rayne as regards her salary, that I should feel that I had brought a communal malediction upon his head. Nor could I fail to see that it was pleasing to more than one of those present to see our rather proper church-going family shown up as being no better than need be. On top of all my other sins I had to carry a great weight of betrayal.

It was finally proposed, and seriously debated at length, that I should be expelled from school. Little as I ever wanted to set foot in that establishment again, this prospect was utterly distasteful. To have been expelled from that school would have been the end of my education, for there was no alternative. And already I had decided that education should be my ladder out of that particular corner of the provinces, that somewhere there lay a larger world with more light and air in its human ambience, and that I should find it and dwell therein. Had school ended, so would that dream have ended. My father pleaded for me then, but the inquisitors, having also discovered the uses of salaciousness, replied contemptuously.

It was in fact Miss Rayne who prevented my expulsion. Her hysteria must have been long since under control by then, and the competent, experienced school-teacher had taken over again. Perhaps she had called to mind other evidences which had come to her attention—lavatory literature, if nothing else—bearing witness to the preoccupation of young children with sexuality. She may even have withdrawn from the prospect of teaching in a school without even *one* child with some aptitude and ambition to learn. She could not see what good it could do either me or the community just to draw the curtains and bury me. She said so. In the end they settled for an innocuous enough formal punishment: I was to be denied participation in the spring musical festival, for which rehearsals were already under way, and which was held at Mafeking and was the great festival of the year in so far as the school children were concerned. All the schools in the division took part. For a few weeks rehearsals were held with all the other children—Larry Willis, who had once been an English choirboy, came specially to train the singers—while I sat huddled in a corner trying to look as though I were casually studying or reading. In the end even that prohibition was removed, because I was the only child who had ever won a prize for the school in a music festival.

Neither parents nor teacher even mentioned the incident again, not even inadvertently, but the skin was a long time in growing back to cover the raw flesh.

Curiously enough an odd tranquillity settled over the school, as if the children had at last eaten their fill. Even the Thorsen-baiting fell off. I had acquired a slight importance, but I was wise now to the human tendency to sentimentalize over victims, even as the ancients used to groom and polish and garland the heifer before they slit her throat. I built a wall of utter indifference between myself and the whole community, and while I believe I behaved in an apparently normal fashion, my neighbours ceased almost to exist for me. Nothing I have recalled so far took place during the two long years I spent in that neighbourhood and in that school thereafter, except for those things which I have mentioned as being reported to me by someone else. I saw nothing for myself. I never tried to be liked or noticed there again. I have several times, while writing this book, wondered what happened to this person or that—what happened to the Thorsen children, for instance, after their mother died? Several of them were still quite young. She must have died just after I started High School in Mafeking when I turned fourteen. I was probably told what happened to them. I would, earlier, have registered the information, but now I can recall nothing. (And did Mrs Thorsen know how grievously her children were tormented for their desperate destitution? I hope they managed to keep it secret from her. She had enough to bear without that.)

Warren left school at the end of that year, having become fifteen, and the school settled into mere humdrum, for which many must have been thankful.

Perhaps ten years later, and far away, I saw Warren Krohlsinger getting on the train I was already on. He wasn't getting into my coach, but the sight of him, even at a distance, filled me with such a panic that I would have got off and waited for the next train, I think, had there been another one to wait for that same day. The train was half empty. There seemed a good chance that he would not come into my coach at all, but he did. He came in, looked around, and came and sat down across from me and started talking pleasantly enough. Once he was there, in front of me, my panic disappeared. The war was just over then. He spoke of his disappointment at not having seen military service, but that neither the army nor the navy nor the air force had wanted his damaged back. He had spent most of the war years on the Alcan Highway, first on its construction out of Edmonton and up to Alaska, then moving heavy freight over it. He told me

63

that he had just been visiting his sister Eileen, who was married now and had two little boys. He pulled out snapshots of the infants, and recounted anecdotes which demonstrated that he had observed them closely and with genuine affection. He said that he was crazy about kids. He said—and he seemed weirdly vulnerable all of a sudden—that he wished he would marry and have kids, but that he didn't believe he ever would, and went on talking about Eileen and her home as if he had just had a dazzling glimpse of paradise and was trying to hold it fast against the erosion of time. He talked as though his sister would have been a complete stranger to me, and I suddenly wondered whether he might not have recognized me. He hadn't. When I told him who I was he was astonished, then pleased. You'd have thought that we had been old pals. He insisted that I go back to the smoker with him for a bottle of beer (illegal, but he had some in his suitcase, and we would just have to keep an eye peeled for the conductor), so we did. He had acquired a number of the elementary social graces, and was a little bit gallant. We were both bound for Edmonton, and he wanted my address there to look me up, suggested that we paint the town together and reminisced about our school days as if they had been perpetual May mornings. I thanked him for his beer and his conversation, but kept my address to myself.

THE NEXT couple of decades after finishing with that school I went through an assortment of incarnations in a variety of geographical and occupational areas, but always returned home fairly frequently, if only for a few days. Then I decided to try a different slice of our celebrated Western Civilization for a while and spent some years in England and France, finally deciding to try to actually settle for a while in

England. It seemed a good idea to celebrate the decision—and incidentally confirm or abandon it—by a visit back to Canada. So, in 1960, leisurely and unaffluent, I set off tourist class by boat and train.

On the boat I fell in with an Englishman, in his early forties I would think, and his considerably younger German wife. His career in electrical engineering had reached a dead end in Britain and he had decided to emigrate to Canada on speculation. He had been there nearly thirty years before, and kept turning over that experience and studying it as though, like the entrails of a sacrifice, it might offer a clue to the future. He had even, he said, decided to try to relive this ancient experience, literally. It would of course be different, his wife being with him this time; he would not be lonely. But with this exception he seemed to be sure that time would have stood still for him, that the same sets would be on the same stage awaiting the same actors for the same roles. He meant to strike out for Southern Ontario first, where he was sure to find work tobacco-picking, or among the small fruits such as strawberries and raspberries. By the autumn they should have saved enough money from this to pay their way on to the prairies, where he would stook grain and help with the threshing—he was lyrical about the prairie harvest and summoned such excitement and sweetness from it as I had not remembered for many a long year. At the onset of winter they would find a livestock farm to settle into where hands would be needed to feed and look after the animals throughout the winter. In the spring they would move on to the orchards of British Columbia. Finally, a year and a second honeymoon hence, they would find themselves in Vancouver with their capital still intact and a year's glorious adventuring behind them, and he would look for something in electrical engineering to settle into.

His attractive wife listened courteously and uncritically to every reminiscence and every plan. I doubt if he knew, any more than I did, whether the prospect bored, pleased or dismayed her.

He had been just seventeen in 1933 when he had defied his father and struck out for Canada at the height of the Depression. Knowing nothing of the farm, he had had no time to learn, but had just got on with it. The climax of his sojourn had come in the Indian summer, after the pitiful harvest, when he had been equipped with a team of horses and wagon, rope, axe, shovel, food and good advice, and sent off to find a coulee running through a wilderness where his employer had turned out a couple of sows with their young pigs in the spring, the coulee being the only place around where it would be fairly certain that not all of the water-holes would dry up during the summer. He was to find those pigs and bring them in. He had gone, located them, constructed some sort of trap, manœuvred the pigs into it with guile and cunning and a Robinson Crusoe satisfaction—only to find that his troubles had not begun. The animals had gone completely wild. He had never dreamt that razorback pork could be so swift and strong, nor that it came equipped with powerful slashing jaws. (About the only time my father ever actually hurried was when he transferred a litter of new-born piglets from the nest of the sow's making to the shed where he wanted them to be: with the piglets screeching in the sack over his shoulder and the old sow squealing murder behind him he could summon an astonishing burst of speed.) At one time, the electrical engineer said, he had sat him down and wept like a child. He had even thought of turning the horses loose to find their own way home while he just went off somewhere—anywhere—away from the scene of his ignominious defeat.

The pretty young wife listened as carefully and neutrally as if she were trying to perfect her already near-perfect English.

Eventually, of course, our hero had got all his pigs loaded and transported, to the amazement of the farmer who, while wanting his pigs, had also been half playing a cruel joke, thinking that the green kid just out from the Old Country would never manage it alone and would have to come crawling back for help.

One puberty rite passed with flying colours, its efficacy apparently dissipated now, after all these years. . . .

It was curiously touching to hear this agreeable, well-spoken stranger conferring romance upon that world of my childhood. I had not, until then, realized how remote that world had become, how utterly banished from my conscious mind—and indeed from the collective conscious mind. The mass media, for instance, are always reviving the Klondike era, or the American Civil War. Noah's Flood, even, is regularly trotted out for inspection of a Sunday, if one moves in the right circles. But the

Depression . . . In Britain it is still yesterday, or at most the day before, but it has just faded away in Canada, so far as I know. My own generation, catapulted from Depression into war with all its high drama, just forgot Depression, having been too young to be much scarred by it. Our elders remember it all right, but spend little time recalling so graceless and unloved a time. The books on the subject, once so topical, have somehow lost most of their pathos. The larger-than-lifes who are summoned forth by the mass media as hooks upon which to hang period reminiscences tend, for that era, to be the Al Capones, the Lindberghs, the Clark Gables, but they exude no miasma of poverty, dust and brute patience.

This Englishman remembered accurately. He knew that it was hard. He remembered the real physical dangers—the limbs and lives at risk jumping on and off moving freight cars, dodging railway authorities and local watchdogs who were set to drive the drifting unemployed from their own special patch as if they were so many plague carriers. He remembered the unrelieved heat and dust of the summers and the frozen winters and the desperate search for work—any amount of any kind of work—for food. But to him this spartan world had been as elemental and satisfying (in retrospect, at least) as mountain climbing or adventuring on oceans in small boats, or even good brisk wars, and he served it up eloquently for his young wife. I soon caught myself acting as a sort of transmitter between him and her, testifying to his accuracy here, prompting him to more recollections there, being visibly impressed with some observation or achievement which her European city-bred experience could not be expected to assess. He had, incidentally, apparently not noticed that this world he was extolling was tolerable only for the young, the healthy and preferably the single: you could probably manage all right with a strong and willing young wife to work along with you, but children, a sick child, doctors' bills, hospital bills. . . .

Having found me useful in verifying his past world, he now started trying to refer his proposed itinerary to me, insisting on advice and comment. In vain did I plead a five-year absence from Canada, detachment from participation in rural life for much longer and a general lack of expertise on economics, agriculture,

67

labour or much of anything else. He insisted. I tentatively suggested that he would have to anticipate the vast mechanization of the farming industry which had followed the war and prosperity, and which had much reduced dependence upon casual farm labour. He seized upon this modest observation as a dog takes to a bone, chewing and worrying at it at length. Eventually, just before we docked in Montreal, he decided abruptly to call off the whole adventure, to catch the first train to Vancouver and electrical engineering and damn the rural pilgrimage. This decision seemed to leave him relieved rather than downcast. It was perhaps not so much good advice he had been wanting as a chance to get himself off that hook on which he had hung himself in some spasm of runaway lyricism. It might simply have been that passive, desirable girl, the efforts he resorted to to arouse some genuine response leading him on and on until he had finally rocketed himself right out of the everyday world to a point where fantasy had taken over and there seemed no alternative to translating it into fact.

On might conceivably feel like catching and transporting wild hogs, single-handed, once in a lifetime. But one couldn't really want to do it twice. Not when one is past forty.

THE ENGINEER and his wife were through Customs and had disappeared for ever from my life long before Customs had finished with me. Indeed everyone had gone, even the very young girl who had somehow not been met and who had finally been taken in tow by the Traveller's Aid lady. I was flattered. For years Customs' inspectors had been passing my bags after one flick of a bored eyeball. However, this time I was carrying a trunk which contained only a suitcase containing another, smaller suitcase. I explained to the nice man that this was to permit me to collect some things I had stored with friends before leaving Canada the last time, and of course he knew at once that *that* was a likely tale. He searched, but found nothing. He called in an assistant. They tapped and listened, like woodpeckers trying to pinpoint a soft-spoken grub. I was grateful for the near superhuman restraint which they showed in not ripping out the linings of the suitcases. Eventually they had to give up —apparently feeling outwitted rather than mistaken—and I, triumphantly, had not even a litter of possessions to manœuvre back into the cases, but had only to snap the fastenings righteously and step out into Montreal where I had lived for a couple of years only a very few incarnations back.

It was June now. Winter, I had thought when I had lived there, was the season for Montreal. Not that I like winter as such very much, but Montreal, like Quebec, looks its best in a clean snow. In summer it is too hot, too traffic-loud, too reeking of trapped poisonous exhaust fumes. But in winter, especially when a heavy snowfall brought traffic to an exhausted crawl or standstill, something as humdrum as wading home from the office through the snow could be a great joy. Great picture-book snowflakes might be drifting through a splendid architecture of elms, or a rising wind might start lifting scarves and ribbons of the clean, feathery masses, weaving them about lighted windows and old grey stone walls. The fact of being able to walk faster, of moving more efficiently, than all those fat dinosaurs of automobiles warmed the heart. That other scourge of Montreal—the creeps, who besiege women for sex or humiliation or whatever, and who seemed thicker on the ground in Montreal than in any other city I have ever known—seemed to hibernate during the winter and one could actually loiter, unmolested, to study patterns of snow-rimed trees against a winter night sky as darkly vivid as if Van Gogh had invented it. Indeed only in the cold—sometimes in a cold too intense for lingering, a cold to dispatch oneself briskly through—could a woman with a taste for solitary walks enjoy any intimacy with Montreal.

There would be no intimacy this trip. I could see that long before the taxi brought me to the house of my friends. It was not just that summer had come, for the taxing heat had not yet settled in, and the gardens were still pleasantly green and rich

69

with lilac. But during the past few years the city had grown tall and strange. Sherbrooke Street—once, I had thought, quite the finest street in Canada with its dignity and reticence—seemed dwarfed and pathetic, just waiting for the knacker. Its towering elms might have been so many pot plants in the path of the oncoming steel and glass towers. When the snow does come in the new tall city it will weave no elegant leisurely patterns, but will whip and sting and blind as it slices through the vast new wind tunnels before it is quickly and efficiently removed. They will discover—if indeed they have not done so already—how to prevent drifts and ice from forming on the hills, and traffic will be able to be everywhere for ever and ever amen, and generations of children who have never heard the hum of a bee or any small summer sound will never hear any small winter sound either.

I visited such friends as still live there from former times. I dropped in—if the expression can apply half way up a great, blunt skyscraper—on the clerical ant-heap, one tiny corner of a vast industrial empire, where I had once been overworked, indispensable and underpaid. The empire had to all appearances survived my departure well enough.

I was glad enough to board the train.

The possibility that the entire journey across most of Canada might seem just commonplace and anticlimactic after the years abroad was soon dispelled. The buildings and cities seemed smaller and flimsier, but the vast landscape was not subject to shrinkage. Indeed it even seemed to have grown since our last encounter. A whole explosion of skyscrapers will hardly make much impression on these landscapes, and even the skyscrapers will dwindle to the stature of toothpicks if you stand well back under a prairie sky. Montreal, Toronto and Ottawa exude some likelihood of a continuing existence in time. Although the tarpaper-and-tin shacks scattered through the wilderness of the Great Northern Shield are fragile enough in themselves, they are firmly embedded in their forests and lake shores: forester, railwayman, or whoever has strung his little clothes-line anywhere between Toronto and Port Arthur, can leave his house in the morning reasonably sure to find it still sheltering there in the evening.

But once the train has climbed to the champagne air of the prairies the land offers no such assurances. Solitary farmhouse and city alike—Winnipeg, for instance—sit precariously, temporarily, on that vast plateau. Whereas Paris, or an English village, may look inevitable, and their sites to have existed only so that men should bring them into being, here department stores, C.P.R. hotels, city halls—whole cities, even—can easily be imagined to disappear, casually and without trace. It is a simple matter to visualize the whole land between the Rocky Mountains and the Great Lakes as empty of man and his dwellings as it is now empty of bison and antelope.

Roads, telephone and power lines, railroads and other exercises in perspective, on the other hand, seem native to the scene. They draw the eye to the vanishing point, to infinity, in a land where all men once were nomads. The great train shouldering its way easily up towards the passes over the Rocky Mountains seems organic to the scene. Here is the home of the automobile that is meant to be lived in—and *is* lived in, for all the pretence people may make of having other, permanent addresses. (No one would subject the Rolls or Mercedes to being lived in: their sarcophagal elegance commemorates the occupant, even as the ornate tomb commemorates his ancestors.) The habitable automobile is not the only reminder of the nomad on these plains. Although the natural-born squalor of the nomad's encampment has not actually been reproduced in our western cities, they are so drab that accident must be ruled out. Only its natural setting makes even Calgary rate a second glance. All public amenities have been firmly kept to a minimum. Parks are mean, sidewalks mostly unshaded by summer and unsheltered by winter. Climate forbids the urbane and leisurely sidewalk café: law and custom have outlawed the cheerful pub, preferring, until very recently, secret orgiastic guzzlings in dark and sordid corners. These have now yielded to expensive lawful public guzzlings in dim and expensive cocktail bars, decorated uniformly in the neo-bordello style. Small wonder that the inhabitants flee their cities as often as possible—only to re-congregate by lake or mountain and set about re-creating the noise, the architectural rubbish, the temporariness of the town.

However, with any luck they *did* enjoy the drive between

the city and the resort—all that lovely distance to hurtle through.

The white natives usually rationalize their travel. They do it for profit, for the fishing, to take pictures, to visit relatives. But the devouring of that monotonous landscape is satisfying in itself, as the Plains Indian still knows, debased as he is. It is said that when he comes into money—real money, as has happened once in a blue moon when oil gushed on a Reserve—he buys a Cadillac or two, depending upon the oil wells and the Indian agent, and he takes off. Between trips he may come back to the old shack, but he doesn't make any gesture towards tarting it up by installing floors or running water or indoor toilet, or anything.

I hope that that tale is true. Someone ought to remember, in the marrow of his bones, that the Great Plains are not mere real estate.

I DEVOUR the journey, the sensations of travelling, the scenes, rediscovering them from a host of previous crossings, trying to record them accurately in the event that this is the last looking. The immaculate, gleaming, air-conditioned, stainless steel, travel-poster, transcontinental diesel streamliner which succeeds—just—in insulating its passengers against the immensity of wilderness and lake and plain is new, but I feel no loyalty towards the draughts and accumulating grime and shabbiness of its forbear. The essential thing is that it stops, as ever, at unlikely gashes in the primeval mosaic of rock, swamp, forest and lake such as Chapleau and White River, that it glides smoothly and purring like a great friendly cat in and out of exotic encampments such as Portage la Prairie and Medicine Hat, where the dazzle of freshly painted little frame houses seems about to summon up wheels and caravan off to some fresh camp ground. Inevitably children wave vigorously as we slide by, the engine's stunted whistle haunting them with visions of larger, brighter worlds beyond the horizons, even as the splendid old steam whistles summoned earlier generations.

Little change outside the windows, except that the birch trees are all dead, their elegant skeletons still standing, bleaching amongst the living woods. Miles upon hundreds of miles, no living birches, except for a few exotics in city gardens, preserved at great expense by elaborate immunization against the killer virus which has apparently swept them from the continent. The birch was the only truly elegant tree native to the plains. Will there be plastic simulated birch-bark now for the school children to use for canoes in their school projects concerning Indians, their folkways and communications?

After a prolonged absence from a country the eye is caught unexpectedly by the most prosaic phenomena. As the train sweeps parallel with streets and highways I find myself watching for cars, registering with astonishment the high incidence of crumpled fenders, bent bumpers and bruised paintwork, mark of the acceptance of obsolescence as a casual fact of life. Even the large, expensive, nearly new car may rush about with unlovely rusting pleats and gashes. What fortunes the British, with their immaculate fenders, must spend on plastic surgery for their cars! At Winnipeg the train stopped so that my window was directly above a parking lot, a little square piled high with neat bales of scrapped automobile metal around which parked cars were nosed in. Like uneasy beasts outside the abattoir, they exuded a sort of exhausted wakefulness, with their unblinking headlamps—even the brand new red Buick convertible.

Montreal to Calgary. It is more than two thousand miles, and there are only four or five genuine changes of scenery: first inhabited, agricultural Quebec and Ontario then the rocky wilderness of the uninhabited Great Northern Shield, then—if one has taken the precaution to travel C.P.R.—some splendid, wild shoreline around Lake Superior, and finally, after a little ambiguity, the sudden surge on to the wheatlands of Manitoba, Saskatchewan and Alberta.

If only the conversation of the inhabitants could show so much variety or be so memorable, or even yield some genuine eccentricity, unless one has the good fortune to encounter some rare, atypical specimen. It is, I suppose, ungrateful to complain of the undifferentiating *niceness* with which the new suburbia-centred society has smothered the heterogeneous crudities of the old pioneering community. And there is no doubt about it: Canadians seem enormously and unmistakably nice. Indeed I found it almost intoxicating, after a lengthy sojourn in France and England, to be once more in the midst of strangers who seemed unsuspicious, not bent on establishing some immediate dominion over the group in which they find themselves; who, without being intrusive, were not afraid to say boo to a strange goose, who evidenced no offence at the close proximity of others of their own kind. Equally it was impossible for me not to notice that nothing had changed; they have almost nothing to say, their talk, geared ever to the lowest common intellectual denominator, is to conversation what muzak is to music. Cheerfully, at the drop of a hat, they will unpack the latest thing in washable, unbreakable, feather-light, finger-tip controlled, instant conversational kit, but there is nothing but toothbrush and handkerchief to produce from it.

The English-speaking Canadian, with a few honourable exceptions, must be the world's most inarticulate expensively educated person. Man striking back at universal education—and winning. Here a successful man—a veritable Pacemaker—will go through life proudly sporting a vocabulary which a Parisian taxi-driver would hardly consider adequate to see him through a normal morning's work. Nor has the rejection of formal English been accompanied by the invention of a brisk and efficient argot, as in Brooklyn or Australia. The average citizen lives complacently with a comic strip vocabulary which is to thought and communication as kiddies' building blocks are to the cathedral at Chartres or the Empire State Building. God alone knows why the Doukhobors have cherished their trauma about education, considering that the State only wanted to vaccinate their children against it for free.

Indeed the one thing likely to ruffle the niceness of one's Canadian travelling companion is the use of a few words of more than two syllables which are unfamiliar to him and are recognized

74

as non-technical terms (technical terms, their incantatory magic widely recognized and highly valued, are okay). He may just start to fidget, and wander off at the first convenient moment with a muttered excuse. He may make it clear that a *faux pas* has been committed, that you have, as it were, drawn a weapon on a peaceable and unarmed civilian. He may request with some spirit that you 'speak English', or break into wit and inquire if you have swallowed a dictionary or something. And yet this same citizen would be undisturbed if you possessed more cars, boats, ranches in the foothills of the Rockies, oil-wells or private planes that he could ever hope to aspire to.

In the midst of the rocks and bush of Ontario I witnessed a spirited skirmish between a couple of embryonic Pacemakers aged, I should say, about six, and shouting vigorously across the centre aisle.

'Two, four, six, eight, ten.'

'Yeah? Ten, twelve, fourteen, sixteen, eighteen, twenty.'

'Yeah? Ten, twenty, thirty, forty, fifty, sixty, seventy, eighty, ninety, a hundred!'

'Yeah? Well, a hundred and ninety-nine!'

'Ha! Nine hundred and ninety-nine!'

'A million!'

'A what?'

'A million, that's what!'

'Yeah? Nine hundred and ninety-nine million!'

'So—who cares!'

'So you care, that's who cares!'

'Yeah?'

'Yeah!'

On them it was endearing. But add forty years, five o'clock shadow, briefcase and there it is: profile of a Pacemaker. With the addition of no more words than could be copied on to a laundry list (and perhaps are, for all I know) they were already equipped to handle sales campaigns, production schedules, distribution studies, miles per gallon, miles per hour, duck-hunting score, sexual encounter score, golf score, capacity for alcoholic beverages and income tax.

Le style, c'est l'homme.

The only other revelation of native sagacity which has

F

remained in my mind from that particular safari came from *Toujours Gai*, who joined us at Regina. She was attractive, smartly dressed, thirtyish, and thoroughly seen off by a swarm of well-oiled contemporaries who were almost certainly 'the office gang'. She loved the train, and all who travelled in her, at sight—nay! she loved the world, the whole wide, warm, wonderful world. I left her in our sleeping car, making the acquaintance of all those wonderful folks. Presently, having presumably conquered that small world, and perhaps a few others *en route*, she caught up with me again in the club car, where she set about stoking up her fading glow. A quiet sing-song was in progress in my end of the car as she came in and she immediately threw in all her reinforcements: the spirit was more than willing and she pulled all stops out, but, unfortunately, the ear was weak to non-existent. Still, her firm hold on a state of bliss was pleasant enough to contemplate.

None the less it was something of a reprieve when a poised, rather elegant young man came in and occupied the seat next to her, for she courteously stopped her singing to acknowledge his presence.

They had exchanged a few inaudible words before her volume control slipped back up to *forte*.

'Say, you've got a sort of a foreign accent. You come from some foreign country?'

Mumble, mumble.

'A student at the University of Toronto! Well! That's real nice! Where'd you say you were from?'

Mumble, mumble.

'You mean British Columbia?'

Mumble, mumble.

'South America! Colombia, South America! No kidding!'

He was apparently not kidding, but she interrupted him.

'You *are* kidding! Why, you're no darkie! I may have had a few, but I can still tell a white man from a darkie.' She broke off then for a too-long moment, to study his swarthy Latin good looks with an earnest intensity that she would have concealed had she been less intoxicated. 'No, you don't come from those darkie places.'

'But Colombia is not——' his voice rose a little too.

'Never you mind, sonny. You have your little joke. I like a joke. I can take a joke. But you're no darkie.'

'But Colombians are not——'

'You're all right. A very nice kid. But you can't fool me. You're no darkie. Well, sweet dreams, anyhow.'

Her vague benediction included us all—perhaps the whole world, darkies as well—as she proceeded, unsteady but still cheerfully authoritative, towards her berth and a well-earned hangover.

It is most unlikely that in a month of Sundays it would enter her togetherness-befuddled brain, drunk or sober, that her conversation with the young man revealed any colour prejudice. Colour prejudice is something that most Canadians assume happens somewhere else. It is one of those pleasantly reprehensible things about the United States, for instance, which help to keep the inferiority sense at bay. If *apartheid* had come to her attention she would, like the great majority of her fellow countrymen, hold impeccably liberal opinions about it—without ever noticing that the Indians around the corner live in a state of accomplished *apartheid* which would be the envy of an Afrikaner nationalist, if only he could bear to do his own manual labour while an idle coloured man was in the neighbourhood. It is unlikely that she would have bothered to know that, until very recently—about the Kennedy era, I believe—when the cruder forms of colour prejudice became unfashionable, not a single one of the better hotels in any city in the whole Dominion of Canada would serve any black person. This was the policy of both the C.P.R. and C.N.R. who, until very recently, monopolized the good-to-luxury hotel business. But had she known—and the thousands like her—it would not have troubled her unduly. The good-natured gregariousness—like perhaps nine-tenths of the vague, well-meaning liberalism in which we are knee-deep—is firmly embedded in vacuity.

But it is unlikely that many of the products of universal education, even in Canada, believe Colombia, South America, to be a 'darkie' place. Indeed it is unlikely that more than a very few citizens ever think at all about Colombia, South America. I don't myself. In this matter I wish to be recognized as belonging to The Overwhelming Majority.

I HAVE BEEN getting off one train or another at Calgary at fairly frequent intervals since 1940, and it has always seemed a good place to arrive in.

The mountains are near and clear as you pull into the outskirts of the city. You know that they are accessible even when not visible. The sky blazes with clarity. The South Saskatchewan, liquid crystal and hardly warmer than the glaciers from which it drinks a few miles to the west, is of the stuff from which technicolor westerns are made; its verges cry out for the silhouette of solitary horse and rider against a setting sun or rising harvest moon, with just a *soupçon* of solo harmonica toying with 'Red River Valley' in the background. (It is therefore not inappropriate that resident oilmen and typists rhubarb about like movie extras in self-conscious attempts at vivacity and colour.) Above all there is the unmistakable feeling of being high above sea level, of an altitude from whence any journey must of necessity be a falling off, a diminishing, descending, lowering experience.

Twenty years before, Calgary had been my jumping-off place, my first bridgehead into the great world beyond farm and school. Here I learned typing and filing, and the fact that although a commercial pecking order certainly exists it justifies no reverence. Here I first knew financial independence. Here I made my first fumbling essays into the mating game, and was first jilted (shadowy young men with whom my relationships seemed fraught with significance one upon a time . . .). The war, although far away from us in distance, quickly caught us up then in its excitement and urgency, jam-packed as the city soon was with young men in uniform, garlanded with the imminent peril for which they were being prepared.

I stayed now a day and a half in Calgary, not looking for vestiges of my own previous existence there, for all that was long since swept away. I had meant to look up friends and arrange visits later in the summer. But it was the First of July, a holiday week-end, and everyone was out of town.

One of the joys of the city, when I had lived there, was its compactness, allowing one to leave it easily to ride or hike or picnic in its spacious outlying territories. I did make a desultory effort to find some landmarks, but all had been obliterated by the

78

bursting city. I found a vantage point from which to study the long, treeless, grassy hills which sweep from away to the north and north-west down to the river. This is the only place where I have ever 'seen' herds of buffalo, 'remembered' them, as it were, streaming in slow, dark, stately avalanches mile after mile from the distant rim of the hills down to congregate at fords during the autumn migrations, as they must have done only a few short years ago. (Funny, I never 'saw' them returning, flowing back uphill in the spring, as they must equally have done.) But this vision was now *kaput*, no doubt about that. Up the giant thighs of the hills groped the gross blunt-fingered paws of suburban housing developments, supermarkets and car parks, motels and gas stations.

It was rather a relief when the rain came on and I could rationally retire to my hotel room to read and soak in the bath and sleep until it should be time to catch the local train home.

Home. Five years ought to allow for enough girding of loins to meet any occasion, but the unnecessary twenty-four hours I had spent in Calgary were in part at least a last reprieve, a forlorn hope that I might just in the nick of time stumble upon that formula to extract the awkwardness and ineptitude which have dogged the ritual of homecoming over the years, whether I lived a hundred miles away and just drove casually down for a week-end, or made some formal pre-arranged excursion from distant parts. Like practically every one of my friends with whom I have talked of homecomings, I carry a little burden of alienation with me which results in vague feelings of guilt with respect to the persons from whom I feel alienated. That, of course, is enough to give a cunning parent the whip hand. I am at least lucky enough not to have to credit my mother with that particular cunning. She is not a blackmailer. We have other problems.

In 1960 my mother was already past eighty—which was one of the reasons behind my journey. And already, over a considerable period of years, she had seemed to be almost petrifying, with certain characteristics steadily sharpening into prominence like an ancient unpruned rose bush past the production of flowers, its wood hardening and toughening, its proliferating thorns the envy of the razor-blade manufacturers. There are those who can take hold of her without bleeding for it, but I am not one of them.

By the time I found myself on the local train bound for Imperia, where Francis would no doubt come to meet me, I was in a familiar state of impending exasperation. I knew with absolute certainty that in a few hours' time I would be trying not to quarrel with my mother and that the effort would be unsuccessful. What should we quarrel about? Goodness knew—goodness, and my mother.

This train, although new, was monumentally uncomfortable. The track zigzagged relentlessly, the engineer was apparently trying to see how fast he could go on the curves, the train jerked and swayed incessantly. The seats had been thoughtfully upholstered in some slippery, plasticated fabric perfect for easy cleaning, so that one had to cling and brace oneself perpetually just to stay on the seat. Indeed to chain smoke, as I did to comfort myself in the circumstances, I found it much easier to light new cigarettes standing than when perched on those seats. I chain-smoked, and focused on my mother as earnestly as a medium bent upon materializing a spirit.

And materialize she did. Moving about the house, getting ready so that when Francis called to take her to the station to meet me he should not be kept waiting. (Since she and Francis concurred in his elevation to head of the family—an elevation which seemed to me a little hasty, as it preceded my father's death, and even his senility, by years—he tends to be treated with an ostentatious courtesy which can be irksome to siblings who have to muddle along without it.) Her pronounced limp gave, as always, great emphasis to her movements, making the simplest gesture authoritative. Although I had not seen the little house she had moved into a couple of years previously, it would be so much like all the other little bungalows that the widowed moved into when their children have left the nest that it offered no obstacle to imagination. Anyhow, my mother could be counted upon to dominate her habitation. There would be an almost finicky precision here, balanced by a remarkable tolerance for plain grime there: the spoons dare not trespass on the space allocated to the forks, nor the forks on the knives, but the whole lot might rest year after year in a drawer which would see neither fresh paper nor duster and become more and more unsavoury unless Alice came and shook the whole place up.

Not only could I see her, I could hear her too, easily, the clatter of the train forming a not unsuitable accompaniment. She was talking to herself, *sotto voce* but incontrovertible, as she had used to rehearse the speech she would let fly at my father when next he opened the door. The delusion of listening intensified so that I actually caught myself eavesdropping, trying to overhear what she was saying so that I could prepare my defence.

It is not a nice position in which to catch oneself. I took myself in hand hastily, smoked furiously and resolved not to quarrel with her at all. It is unbecoming at my age still to be shouting at a parent. I thought upon Gandhi, and the world as illusion. I thought that it takes two to make a quarrel. I took, in short, a complete inventory of my defences and came up with the sad reflection that had I been capable of coping with the situations presented by my mother I would presumably have learned long ago the knack of doing so. I had not the faculty of impressing her. But then, what *had* impressed her—since the 1904 Exposition in St Louis, that is?

With a sudden chill, with something not far from anguish, I hoped that she was not moving back towards that epoch, not to dwell there. As my father's memory deserted him it was the things nearest in time that receded first, so that I, the youngest child, was the first to slip from his recognition. He continued to remember me, in a curious way; remembered that such a person as I existed, but was puzzled to establish any connection between her and the flesh and blood there before him. 'Oh, your name is Heather too, is it?' he would say. 'We have a Heather. Our youngest girl. She travels a lot—we don't see much of her any more. . . .' His voice would be filled with regret. In those days my mother would often erupt into our conversation (if such it could be called, for he was so deaf that he could hear little that I said), and she would state in that incontrovertible voice which he *could* hear, 'But *this* is Heather. This *is* our Heather!' He would pause, puzzled and courteous, and after she had thumped off again about her business he would continue: 'You don't happen to know her, do you?'

'Yes,' I would say. 'Yes, I know her.'

'Do you see much of her? Is she well?' he would ask.

'She is very well,' I would say. 'She's coming home for a vist soon. Very soon.'

'That will be nice,' he would say. 'We don't see much of her these days. . . .'

Finally, even that recollection escaped him and he lived further and further in the past, talking of aunts and neighbours I had never heard of, of schoolfellows and events of seventy years and hundreds of miles away. And my mother went on cooking and mending and washing for him, and watched over him like a hawk, for he would suddenly slip away to hunt for a cow that went missing forty years before, or to repair a fence torn down even longer ago, in another country. In the rolling, bushy country he could have been lost for hours, or days, and his deafness would have prevented his picking up signals from searchers. But my mother went right on correcting him to the very end, too, fiercely rejecting the fact of his mind's decay. She is not one of your meek acceptors.

The possibility which I briefly entertained that she might be scheduled to suffer his alienation shocked me. I suppose that I have always assumed her to be indestructible. Certainly a great deal of her has remained intact through erosions that would have picked the flesh clean off more delicate bones long since. Feet, for instance. Hers are the most grossly deformed feet I have ever seen. Her bunions must have ached like teeth and without respite for years and years. Her feet, which had been an odd shape to begin with, were certainly not made to order for pioneering. Whether she had ever been able to get shoes that actually fitted properly I don't know, but certainly after she came to Canada and her shoes came from Timothy Eaton's mail order store in Winnipeg, a thousand miles away more or less, the shoes came only in standard sizes to fit standard feet. She sometimes kept the first impossible pair they sent because what they sent to replace those returned were never an improvement. On feet like those, Napoleon's *élite* guard would never have got beyond the frontiers of France, let alone to Moscow, and yet this unheroic little woman had got on to them every single day of her long life and walked miles and miles every day just to keep the household going. Sometimes she had help with the heavier work and sometimes not, but feet were on duty whether or no. The same with her rheumatism and neuritis. She did not suffer them in silence.

82

We all knew all about it. We had no chance of not knowing. But we are at least spared the martyr's special legacy to her loved ones—that *post-mortem* discovery that for years on end they have been unwittingly destroying her, and only now, when it is too late, they must eternally reproach themselves—et cetera, *ad infinitum* and *ad nauseam*. My mother has had the decency to present her well-kept accounts on this side of the Great Divide.

Accounts . . .

What one was she preparing for me even now, to be presented in a scant two hours'—Good Lord! a scant half-hour's—time?

Damn! I had travelled all these thousands of miles from London, at great expense, given the state of my exchequer, and although she was not the only reason for my voyage she was a principal one. And she was genuinely pleased that I was coming. Why couldn't we, just this once, not quarrel about anything?

THE SLIGHT break in the voice, the modest display of tears—just a misting over of the eyeballs, really—with which my mother greets things like the return of the prodigal daughter can be a provocation in themselves. Before that scant moisture would have had time to evaporate—and there was a fine drying wind blowing too—she would have her guns trained on me. If *I* knew that, *she* must know it too. I can't recall the formal words of greeting, the polite inquiry as to the kind of trip I had had, although they were surely spoken and acknowledged. I was listening for—ah, there it was!—that excessively polite, patient, reasonable tone of one who is trying *so* hard to understand just how on *earth* anyone could . . .

'I beg your pardon?'

'I said that we just couldn't help being surprised that you

should have made us come all the way to Imperia to meet you, that's all,' she said.

'Why? What difference does it make, Imperia or Regalia?'

'Difference? Why, nearly six miles difference, that's the difference. It's nearly six miles farther to Imperia.'

'But you've got the car. . . .' My brother's ancient unwashed Buick, accustomed to carrying himself, wife, ten children, mother, spare parts for machines, tractor fuel, vast quantities of food, etc., looked in fact as though the extra six miles might well finish it off, but then it had looked that way five years, several thousand miles and three or four fewer children ago. Some defect in its obsolescence, I guess.

'Francis is pretty busy these days,' said my mother firmly, thereby putting my journey across the Atlantic, up the St Lawrence, and more than two thousand miles of solid Canada into perspective.

Francis made his contribution to the conversation, and it was possibly a joke. 'A lucky thing for you it rained last night,' he said. 'Too wet to cut hay this morning so I brought this in and got it welded.' He tapped the crankshaft or drive shaft or whatever it is that this generation of farmers is always having welded.

I reminded myself that my mother *was* pleased to see me, that we were just going through that apparently essential ritual, and that afterwards we would settle into an amicable lack of communication.

'All these years you've managed to come home without making us come all the way to Imperia for you,' she said. 'I don't see why you should want to start now.'

'It's not a question of *wanting*. There's no train direct from Calgary to Regalia any more.' I felt a treacherous surge of relief. How many times over the years have I not brightened up at the prospect of the ritual abruptly culminating through the exercise of rationality, like a medieval devil vanquished by the sign of the cross!

'Well, we know that,' said my mother serenely. 'It's been—what—two years now since they closed that line? Two years last March, wasn't it, son?'

'That's right,' said Francis. 'Two years last March.'

'We've known all along that there was no train from Calgary to Regalia,' said my mother.

Rather half-heartedly we went through the possibility that I might have made the hundred-and-twenty-mile journey from Calgary to Regalia a two-day venture, stopping overnight at a depressing hotel in a dreary little town near the outskirts of limbo so as to get up at six the next morning to catch the train which did the last fifty miles to Regalia. But I noticed that she was only using her minor-skirmish voice through this detour, and she didn't drop that until she demanded to know why I had found it necessary to come through Calgary at all. Now *she* would have come to Edmonton, and from Edmonton there was a good train service direct, every day, to Regalia.

'I have come to visit you after five years abroad,' I said. 'I needn't have come at all. But why should you complain about the route I chose to travel by? What difference can it make?'

'You have to travel Canadian Pacific when you come to Calgary,' said my mother ominously.

'So?'

'I have no use for their Canadian Pacific.' The constellation of her disapprovals is almost inevitably associated with 'them'. 'They' are never precisely designated, but it is 'their' Social Credit Party, 'their' C.B.C., 'their' Roman Catholic Church. 'Daddy and I travelled on their C.P.R. nine years ago when we went down home for the last time,' she said. ('Daddy' means my father—her own was always designated as Papa; 'down home' means Iowa, whereas her place of residence is just 'home'.)

She proceeded to tell me the saga of that trip, with emphasis on the iniquities of the C.P.R. They had travelled over quite a number of mid-western states and visited almost everyone they had ever known or been related to in any way. I suppose I had heard the story before, but would hardly have remembered as her recitals tend to be straightforward railway time-tables—with comparisons between the published and the actual experienced time-table—laced with weather and crop reports; whatever might pass as human interest incidents or observations are kept to an austere minimum. I did not trouble to listen to her very intently, but I gathered that the whole trip had been a triumph of comfort and realized expectation, except for that stretch done via the C.P.R. between an utterly obscure whistle-stop in North Dakota and an even more obscure place in Saskatchewan where

85

my clergyman cousin Harvey—who rather specialized in obscure missions at that time—was living.

Any one of scores—hundreds, even—of those branch lines which had thrust crooked fingers from a minor centre of habitation into the almost blank spaces on the map of Canada might have provided my mother with her dismal tale. The C.P.R., as I knew from experience, had no monopoly of such services. Once these lines had been the Happy Hunting-Ground of all the bronchitic old steam-engines and rusted threadbare rolling stock in the country—maybe in the world—and there had been no nonsense about coddling the passengers. If a wash basin was provided on the train only an incurable optimist would have hoped to find water to put in it. The seats would have left saddle sores on a tenderfoot. When the train stopped long enough to take on coal and water the passengers were welcome to venture into the uninviting little town to hunt for food which (with luck) they might find. (I thought of my vague, leisurely old father trying to galvanize himself into the sort of action necessary to find provisions, and hoped that a kind hostess had burdened them with parcels of sandwiches and fruit.)

Most of those old pioneer lines which have not been modernized are closed down and mouldering away now. None the less, there seemed little enough reason for my mother to complain of stumbling on to one in the recent past. The line may well have been so obscure that the C.P.R. had lost track of it entirely and had consequently forgotten either to wind it up or to modernize it. And anyhow such trains had been, quite simply, a part of the pioneer world in which she had lived for so long and, like her, some had survived past their own era. She might quite reasonably have done a Betjeman and romanticized the whole business. I reflected on this and, unsympathetic, just left my ears turned on enough to let me know when the recital of the inglories of the C.P.R. should be finished and life could settle down to normal.

It lasted through our leaving the station, collecting Francis's vast order of groceries and my cigarette supply of panic proportions, it accompanied us out of the inconsequential untidiness and magnificent lilacs of Imperia and on to the familiar washboard of the fourth-rate unpaved road which had once been completely familiar when I had lived close enough to drive home quite regularly for week-ends. We charged along now like the Light Brigade, apparently bent on achieving a definitive end. Lack of good brakes or good steering or good road has never dimmed my brother's enthusiasm for speed, and his farmer's concern for crops and the progress of the season's work on both sides of the road reduces his interest in the road itself to a minimum. In short, he drives like a farmer. It is a fact that he has never had a serious accident. None the less I could have wished that my mother's recital was really absorbing. As it was I had to try to focus upon—and make do with—scenery.

An undistinguished procession of fields, really green with the lush growth of an unusually rainy June. Country which, like many people, needs to be known intimately to be loved. Little grassy mounds—we have always dignified them by calling them hills—rise from little water-filled sloughs. Brush patches cover the north-facing slopes with poplar, willow, saskatoon, pin cherry, choke cherry. Silver wolf willow on dry clay hillsides that face the sun. Buck brush wherever the grassland has been over-grazed. Everything looks inconsequential after the splendid architecture of English trees or the hardwoods of Quebec and Ontario—but that anything survives year upon year in this climate is a miracle, and the brush, once you know it, is quite companionable.

My mother went on and on and on, like a mammoth Hollywood epic.

Finally, our fourteen-mile journey completed, there was a brief intermission while Francis's wife Marion came out to the car to greet us and to show me such of the younger children as I had not seen or been able to recognize. I was able solemnly to assure all that I had met before that they had grown enormously since I had last seen them. Then Marion organized her brood into a disorderly retreat into their house, and my mother ushered me into hers, which was less than a stone's throw from the other.

She was pleased with her modest little house, and had cause to be. It was a vast improvement over the one she had wrestled with for the preceding forty-five years: warm, without leaks or draughts, sensibly laid out, good kitchen cupboards—a little too high for my mother, of course, she being somewhat less than five feet tall, and nothing ever being designed for that stature. With an inexhaustible supply of grandchildren at hand to look after the rougher chores—carrying wood and water, emptying ashes, keeping the grass down around the door—she was really set up to her heart's content. She had, as I had known she would, already stamped her dwelling with her unmistakable habits of housekeeping.

But my gratification with her new abode was tempered by the knowledge that she had not done with me yet. There had been no finale sounded to the saga of the C.P.R., and now there was no passing scene or other analgesic distraction. Here I would be face to face with the music.

And I was soon summoned to the table. Not to eat or drink, although a cup of tea or coffee would have been a civilized gesture after my journey. No. Two bulky, impressive railway time-tables were lying open on the table, with figures encircled with red and blue ink.

'What I can't see', she said, 'is why you deliberately went so far out of your way. All that extra distance.'

I muttered something rude, inaudibly.

'You can see it there for yourself,' she said. 'It's 2,240 miles from Montreal when you come by Calgary, by the C.P.R. If you had come C.N., through Edmonton, it would have been only 2,202 miles.'

'Well,' I said, 'I wasn't walking, was I?'

'That's thirty-eight miles farther. Thirty-eight.' She was severe, as if they were spinach left on my plate.

'I wasn't walking,' I repeated. 'I wasn't walking, I didn't get a single blister. It didn't cost any more—I got more miles for my money. I wouldn't have saved any money travelling C.N., you know. I'd have paid exactly the same and been carried only—what was it?—2,202 miles for it. Why pay all that to travel only 2,202 miles, when you might have had 2,240 miles?' But I couldn't stop. I never can manage to stop, with her, at the critical moment. 'In fact, why travel at all? I don't really like it much, you know. I might as well have stayed in England instead of coming all this way and wasting all that money just to be engulfed in twaddle. I should have known better. Twaddle! Twaddle!'

'Well!' she said. 'You needn't fly off. There's no point in—I was only trying to help.' She was suddenly composed and cheerful, setting a badly needed example of serene good temper, inviting common sense to prevail. The ritual was finished for her once I had been prickled into displaying something which might be classified as an infantile tantrum. Reduced to the age of ten, nursing a mute hostility. I loathe being ten. There is nothing to recommend the age of ten. Already I'm itching to catch the next train out—any train, going anywhere, so long as it will carry me back to my late thirties.

TIME WAS when my mother, as befits a lifelong member of the Women's Christian Temperance Union, could smell an addiction a mile off. She had had strong views, for instance, about old Mrs Varma, who had formerly occupied the little house which now bulged with Francis's family. I suppose that Mrs Varma suffered from migraine. My mother, who was not subject to headaches, always spoke of them as 'headaches', in quotation marks, and thought the pulling of blinds and silencing of the telephone bell (which would clatter all the day long, there being some fifteen to twenty subscribers, all of whose calls jangled every phone) pretentious, if not worse. As for aspirin—well, it was rumoured that Mrs Varma took up to a dozen or fifteen in a single day! 'I reckon she drugs herself,' was my mother's verdict, spoken invariably in her dropped, confidential voice. She herself will tell willingly how she has taken aspirin only twice during her long life, and then upon someone else's urging, and had consequently suffered more from the effects of the drug than from the malady which invoked such a remedy.

She has always had strong opinions about tea and coffee, and has sheltered us from possible narcosis by brewing them so wan and listless as to constitute no conceivable menace. Francis christened her tea 'scairt water' years ago. There is, so far as I know, no epithet to convey the odium of her thin coffee.

When radio first appeared in our neighbourhood she was quick to note the likelihood of auditory addiction and condemned the practice of leaving the set running to grind out continuing background noise. We were rather late in acquiring a radio ourselves; I was already away at school, or possibly even working. But I can remember that, at home, one's radio listening was according to rule, and the rule, which was reasonable enough, was that we could listen by deliberate plan to something specifically selected from the published programmes, but there must be no 'shopping around' from station to station on spec. Also, when we listened we had to shut up and *listen*. Her own passions were always news bulletins and weather reports. I believe that it was a matter of real regret to her that every station within reach broadcast these at the same time—on the hour only—as that meant that she could tune in to only one of the four or five that would otherwise have been available.

When we arrived at her house it was not news time. And then of course there had been the matter of my indiscretion with railways to clear up, followed by a few genuine, if faltering, attempts at pleasant chat. So the radio was not turned on immediately. But finally the hour rolled around and with it the news—her favourite old folksey, very local newscast which can even include tittle-tattle about lost pussy cats or wisecracking budgie birds. It sounded identical to the last newscast I had listened to with her five years previously—it may be that the station just compiles an almanac of 'news' for each day of the year, like those books of religious meditations, which will do year after year. The plot never changes, nor, apparently, do the characteristics of the characters—only the names.

Soon the newscast was over, and the weather report and forecast, and the break for station identification. Came the breathless, synthetic excitement of the disc jockey with the rousing news that we had only to stay tuned to good old station XXXX to be entertained by the top twenty and nothing but the top twenty over and over all the day long, to say nothing of the goddam night. I awaited with confidence the firm parental hand on the adjacent

90

switch. But the top twenty, starring 'Chain Gang'—or was it 'Mule Train'?—got under its inexorable way without so much as a diminution of volume, to be punctuated only by a flatulence of commercials at regular intervals. News and weather every hour on the hour, top twenty, commercials, news and weather. Over and over and over and over. In that tiny house, with that volume, it was like being imprisoned in the amplifier of a juke box. I protested. She defended herself, but had the grace to reveal some embarrassment.

I suggested a compromise: she might have her newscasts every waking hour if only I might be allowed to turn the sound down in between. She agreed reluctantly. She admitted readily that she had no liking for the music of the hit parade; she did not actually know what songs were on it, could not have hummed one tune or recited one line from the whole bagful. But when we tried out the diminished noise it was not a success. She started immediately, and quite involuntarily, trying to hear clearly. It irritated her as if she were starting to go deaf. Nor would she turn to another station: only this one provided noise that made no demands on attention.

She could not, she complained, a little sorry for herself, stand a silent and empty house all the time. I forebore mentioning that the house was not empty when I was in it. As to the silence, I could hardly swear to keep that dissipated between us: not since I was little enough still to enjoy playing checkers and dominoes and chinese checkers with her had we two ever managed to dissipate silence mutually. I would, by direct questioning, extract a little factual information from her about the neighbourhood families, but inevitably it would be only such vital statistics as do not interest me at all: the numbers and ages of children in each household, with which of Francis's children these offspring were classmates, how they stood in relation to Francis's children in class (inevitably below), who had married since I had last been home, who had died. Facts. As to the world I inhabit, she was devastatingly incurious about that. She was not curious about France or England, or what I might have been doing therein.

I yielded over the noise question. She really would have turned the wretched radio off if she could have, I thought.

And the wonder was not that she had yielded to noise, but that she had been so long in doing it, given her natural antipathy to silence and solitude. Those last years before my father died, when they still lived in the old isolated house and hardly ever saw anyone but Francis, who dropped in frequently but only for a moment, when beside the two old people there was for long periods only a silent old cat and a silent old dog (not even a house dog), when my father did little more than wake up, shuffle the pages of book or newspaper, uncertain whether he had just read or was reading or intended to read the item he found in his hand, and doze off again, she might easily have given in to radio. He was too deaf and too indifferent to have noticed. But she didn't, not until after he was dead. And then I guess that she decided upon a holiday from Setting An Example.

It was sad, of course, after she had come so far with flying colours. A small ignoble voice inside me said something about 'false colours', and rehearsed the magisterial way in which she had lectured and corrected mere mortals like myself in her heyday, pushing principles which had perhaps been beyond her own capacities. But any tendency towards unfilial—or any other kind of—mirth was short-lived. Like the veriest alcoholic on the skids reaching for that early morning drink which is supposed to shrink the menace of the looming day, she reached for her lift— that radio switch—at 07.30 hours every morning. As I was sleeping on the sofa it was, as it happens, about three feet from my sleep-sodden ear.

I did not fortunately have to spend much time in that house. When I had first written of my projected visit my mother had immediately asked if I would travel with her 'down home' to Iowa. Her brother Frank was dying. He had already been bed-ridden with Parkinson's disease for some time, and his periods of lucidity were said to be decreasing steadily in number and duration. She wanted to see him alive, but no longer felt able to make the journey alone. I had agreed to travel with her, and obviously we should not delay. I stayed in her house only long enough to renew acquaintance with Francis and Marion, and my sister Alice and her Welsh husband Harry, and to consider again the natural world into which I had been born.

Indeed it was pleasant, for a change, to be able to take almost immediate refuge with Alice and Harry without worrying lest my mother should detect some unseemly haste in my enthusiasm to be elsewhere. Over the years their home had offered just the sort of easy, cheerful communication I could never manage at home. My mother already had enough complaints about Alice. I need not generate another by obviously preferring life in their hospitable, unpainted house with its one small and two tiny rooms, standing on their marginally economic farm. Alice, for instance, married a man with just that little bit more charm than repectability can swallow—a man, too, who has heeded those lilies of the field who toil not. Harry *does*, in fact, toil—off and on he's done quite a lot of it during his life—but only if there is nothing better and more sociable to engage in. If there is one text the good, right-living, industrious Protestant like my mother has never managed to assimilate it's that one about those damned lilies.

I accept, but cannot remember, that I was bunged upstairs to sleep with Alice, twelve years my senior, when my infant brother was born. As I was only about a year old at the time, and as proper waterproof breeches for infants were still in the womb of technology (although simple practical things like battleships had been around for ages), I gather that her bed was subsequently not exactly one of roses. Alice does not maintain that this close early association of ours was one of the highlights of her modestly eventful life, but we have none the less managed cheerful if never very intimate relations over many years now.

So I was saddened to find a shadow fallen ominously over her family, a shadow cast by an unusually bitter quarrel, which started with Francis, but which my mother had unfortunately entered into with quite unseemly zest. A sort of doubt had settled over the whole family, eating away at the idiosyncrasies which made them blessedly unique.

Typically, however, Marion was on good terms with everybody. Marion is tall, big-boned, soft of voice and slow of movement, with the dazzling red hair Hollywood reserves for fire-eating colleens scheduled for spanking by the hero in the final reel. If Hollywood had the stamina to follow its colleens through a few more reels they would, in all probability, be found swarming with infants, too, all of whose nappies they wash and meals they prepare and measles they nurse single-handed, and Barry

93

Fitzgerald turning up like a Decency League leprechaun to perform the annual christening, faith and begorrah. This Marion could share with the Hollywood colleen. Walls bulge and roofs lift with the force of the private little population explosion which she and Francis have conjured up.

I cannot pretend to know Marion, barricaded as she is behind serried ranks of children, all of whom need her attention all of the time, so that only a tiny portion of her is ever available to communicate with the outsider. However, like all the rest of my family I never cease to marvel at her ability to live tranquilly with her mother-in-law. For there sits my mother in her little house, only a few yards from Marion's house, surveying, as from a control tower, practically everything that is going on out of doors in the farmyard and garden. Frequently she finds it necessary to pick up her phone and call Marion to tell her that Donald is wading into that puddle behind the chicken house and she thinks he is in over the tops of his boots already, or doesn't Marion think she ought to get after Gerry, who hasn't done a tap of weeding in over half an hour? She has been sighting him against a telephone pole and he just hasn't budged an inch. Et cetera. And there is Marion cooking, washing up, cleaning house, laundering, supervising homework and chores, mending, administering first aid, et cetera, for some twelve or thirteen children, of whom four or five have been of pre-school age for more than a decade (including a small baby, one just learning to walk and one vigorous and suicidal toddler). If she does manage to get some help in the household it never, oddly enough, stays long—although it invariably feels badly about leaving her with all that work to do. . . . Nevertheless she gives her mother-in-law an unfailingly patient, unhurried hearing and a civil answer. Fortunately my mother seems content to have reported the incident and made suggestions and apparently does not require action to be taken on then. It almost never is.

So far as I can see, Marion and her mother-in-law actively *like* one another. It is very impressive.

I HAD ONLY to set foot outside my mother's house to be confronted by a stairsteps of grinning youngsters—everyone able to walk purposefully from Francis's house the few yards to my mother's, but not yet old enough to be away at school. They didn't clamour for attention, just shyly hoped to be invited in or to be taken for a walk or anything else that might promise a little novelty.

But the poverty of the universe they served up to me was depressing. *We*, as I could recall, could trundle a visiting aunt on a major safari at the drop of a hat and did so whenever an aunt was so intrepid as to visit. In any season, good year or bad, there was a multiplicity of major exhibits: rare wild flowers, birds' nests, berries, elaborate tunnels cut into snowdrifts. And then of course we had the animals: dozens of horses and milk cows, all with their names and their known characters and places in the hierarchy of farm and herd. And pigs and sheep and chickens and geese—including evil old ganders who lay in wait to bully children, of whom I was always the smallest and most easily routed. Ducks, dogs, cats—not just spoilt pets, but working cats, expected to keep mice and gophers to a decent minimum in the vicinity of the farm buildings. I suppose that mine was almost the last generation, in our civilization at least, for whom the ancient symbiotic relationship of man with animal kept its meaning intact; the last generation for which, during childhood, the animals worked their immemorial magic of mediation between child and the earth. Henceforth, however, animals may be chemical processes producing protein, mere pets, performers of tricks, curios and exhibits, tourist attractions, or emblems of conspicuous consumption, but they cannot conceivably mediate between anything and anything.

Francis's children marched me off gleefully enough to inspect the beavers at work on their lodge in the slough north of the house. Pleasant enough, if smacking somewhat of the out-and-out tourist attraction. But they had, it seemed, exhausted their resources then and there. It being the first week in July, I asked if they knew where to find some wild tiger-lilies. They did, as it happened, but they hadn't known that wild tiger-lilies are an event.

The factory farming of animals had not yet arrived on my

brother's farm. None the less I could see that Francis's children—and probably most farm children—have become suburbanites in all but name. Farm machines have become too dangerous, the chemicals too unpleasant, for children to mess about the farm and be integral to its processes any more. For all their involvement in his work, father might must as well be catching the seven-forty every morning to his office or factory in the city.

The children did tentatively offer me the spectacle of the milk cow and a nondescript heifer who was pastured with her to keep her company. But *a* cow is nothing—like *a* lawyer. A cow is a social animal and only becomes herself—serene, cunning, lewd, bossy or downright tyrannical—in society. They showed me too the horse which Francis kept for his semi-annual work among the beef cattle, but they signalled its existence without any display of enthusiasm or rapport. The older boys had licence to ride it, but as their riding was gratuitous and not integral to their lives the horse remained nothing but a toy. In my day we were far too dependent upon our animals to feel superior to them or to sentimentalize them.

The Second World War changed everything.

Until then, coming home for holidays from school or office involved only a simple matter of picking up familiar threads; making the acquaintance of the new colts and the new heifers joining the milking herd, inquiring into the casualties. Both my brothers being at home on the farm with my father meant three men working full time, plus old Morgan to milk a cow or two at either end of the day. The economy was still not much more than barter, with money scarce as hen's teeth and already bespoke for debts before it even got into the pocket.

Then overnight there was the War. Wilbur was off to the air force, never to return. Money put in a shy then positive appearance. Labour disappeared, and the men stopped spending endless hours and days coaxing a little more life into ancient machinery and spent money for replacements which actually worked. Suddenly there was a tractor on the farm; not a new one, not even one in the first flush of youth, but still it enabled one man to do the work formerly done by two men and eight horses. And so our beloved horses—of no particular breed or distinction—were no longer bred. My father's loyalty to them saved them from the knacker, but they lost status, just loafing around, eating grass and waiting to die of natural causes.

I suppose that in a way my father's fate ran parallel with theirs. He was already sixty-eight in 1940, still wiry and instinct with unobtrusive powers of endurance, with all faculties intact other than being somewhat deaf—to the end of his life he could read indifferent print for hours on end aided only by a pair of glasses with magnifying lenses he had bought from Woolworth's. He could have kept on top of his situation for another eight or ten years, had the situation remained constant. But his adaptability had atrophied. His slow, fumbling, stiffened arthritic fingers were not only useless around a tractor—they were a menace. His reflexes did not allow for speed. Soon the management of the fields became Francis's prerogative, with my father increasingly relegated to mere chores and odd jobs. Francis naturally became increasingly assertive and, somewhat less naturally, my mother hastened to lose her neutrality and promote son over husband in almost everything. My father put up a stout, unobtrusive, quiet rearguard action, but was obliged to yield his authority little by little—although he kept his bank account sacrosanct, and rendered no accounts to anyone, until the day of his death. It would be an impertinence to think of him as in any way pitiable.

I thought at the time that there was some unseemly haste in the manner in which my father's shoes were being filled while he was still in them, but experience told me that he needed no allies and that a spectator who insists upon climbing into the ring and throwing punches about is nothing but a pest. And I knew too, whatever my sympathies, that had I been in Francis's shoes I too would have been driven to shake off my father's administration.

My father was better educated than either of his sons. Somewhat to his regret, I think, neither of them showed any interest in formal education, and were accordingly allowed to leave school when they reached the required age. But both of them had a natural instinct for technology, Francis's running towards the techniques of farming, Wilbur's towards mechanics—he tinkered with electricity and all kinds of motors with considerable success. My father, whose mouldering college textbooks bore witness to a modestly good grounding in the humanities as well as some science, had a curious half-grasp of the meaning of science such as one sometimes still encounters in English humanities' academics, although my father's attitude was not at all hostile. He had for instance obviously heard of genetics, and so he put his knowledge to use. He crossed a strain of milk cow with a strain of beef animal, and forthwith concluded that he had produced something which provided Niagaras of milk, and whose male calves grew into hulking great slabs of beef. He never noticed that the result in fact was a derisory milk production from cows whose calves never did become generously fleshed.

But Francis noticed.

And so the day arrived when I came home to visit and promptly set off, as was my wont, for a tramp through my favourite pasture, and came upon a herd of cattle which were all of an identifiable breed. Beef cattle, in fact, the labour and financial incentive to produce milk having disappeared. They did not impress me very favourably, being obviously anonymous, nameless beasts—beasts which did not make regular daily migrations up to the barnyard for milking and which consequently were allowing all the familiar and intimate paths through field and wood to become overgrown and slovenly and alien. However, I felt no animosity towards the animals themselves on that cool, crisp, blustery spring day. I was not in any event very near to them, and my path did not take me towards the herd but past it, at a little distance. But instead of contenting themselves with lifting their heads in the immemorial, mild, bovine inquiry as I walked quietly on my way, one of the damn fools lifted its tail, let out a bellow and took off for parts unknown. The whole herd thundered after, like something out of a film about Texas. In fact they did not stop until they had gone through two fences and were belly deep in a neighbour's oat-field. I don't know that I have ever been more deflated in my life, to be treated like a Thing from Outer Space by the family cows.

Francis had to spend a whole precious day rounding them up and mending fences and reporting the incident, with apologies, to the oat-field-owning neighbour, so it was pretty stoic of him, overworked as he was, to show no annoyance about it. But our mutual mother, whose metamorphosis into a one-member

Society for the Protection and Preservation of Francis first became clearly visible to me on that day, was astringent. If I *had* to go walking in the pasture—in which I had no visible pressing business—her theory was that I should have known better than to wear therein a skirt and brightly coloured headscarf to blow in the brisk spring breeze. The beef herd, she felt, was accustomed only to trousers. (The funny thing was that for years she had been campaigning to see me wear a skirt around the place now and again, as she has never agreed with me about the natural superiority of slacks for everyday wear.) Having to submit to such a lecture on the psychology of cows from my mother, of all people, was little to my liking. Cows had always been one of the few subjects on which she had not pretended to be authoritative. She knew nothing, or next to nothing, about cows. She had never herded them or milked them, or climbed aboard to find how long it would take to be thrown off, or anything. She had never even known which cow was which, except for old Dinah, the solitary recognizable Holstein.

After that, trousers or no trousers, I visited my old haunts only as a cautious intruder, giving a wide berth to all domestic fauna. But I was still under the impression that my relations were good with the wild life. It was some years before the gulls disabused me on that score.

On that occasion I was home for a few days during early May. Conscientiously avoiding all livestock, I indulged myself by visiting a tiny lake which had always been my childhood's Special Place. The lake, possibly spring fed, had not dried up during the worst of the drought. It is cradled in poplars and cottonwood trees of the variety which gives off a fragrance more fresh and delicate even than the fragrance of pines. I had spent hours and days walking, loitering, picking berries in sight of it. And when I used to ride after the cows I tried my best not to find them until I had had a good look for them around the lake—a really thorough look, lacking only the turning over of flat stones to see if they might not be hidden underneath with sundry ants and beetles.

The lake, like every permanent body of water on the plains, however small, has always attracted its quota of the small black-headed gulls which I have always found so attractive. Probably they have no more contact with mighty waters than I (or do they winter, perhaps, in the Gulf of Mexico? It has never occurred to me to wonder where they wintered . . .). Anyhow, their cries, much as the old steam locomotive whistles, were always a summons to dream of far places and melancholy joys. And they rose magnificently to the oncoming storm, those gulls, planing in elegant white patterns against dark and brooding clouds, punctuating the distant mutter of thunder with Cassandra cries. A Wagnerian lot, really—and probably better kept at a romantic distance where their vulgarity was not visible.

Anyhow, on my day in May a satisfactory scatter of them rose from the lake and its reedy north verge as I left the cover of the poplars on the hill and descended towards the water. In the light of all my past experience I knew that they were almost as familiar as poultry, and having circled for a few ritual minutes they would settle casually again on the water, satisfied that I was going about on my innocuous lawful occasions. But, of course, under the new rural regime no human being on foot had been near their haunts for months—maybe years. It was nesting season too. Suddenly screaming gulls were hurtling about my ears like so many dive-bombers. I felt not only the rush of air from their wings, but the brush of stiff dry wing-tips. Had I come amongst them as a needle-nosing naturalist or tourist I should have been prepared for hostility. But I was in fact on a pious pilgrimage to the Nursery of my Tender Years, and felt as orphaned and disconsolate as though the teddy bears and woolly lambs had descended from the wallpaper to hurl maledictions upon my head. I suffered myself to be driven off.

And so it happened, now, that I sat in my mother's little juke-box of a house for a few days wondering whether or not I should visit the old farm. It was there, its nearest corner only half a mile away. I had passed the gate where the mailbox used to stand during our drive from Imperia. I passed and repassed it every time I went to see Alice and Harry. I would have dearly loved a few hours' intimacy with it again. . . . I meditated upon it and meditated again, with 'Chain Gang' or 'Mule Train' or whatever it was jerking on and off in my ears. I thought of the empty old house, too frail and insubstantial to memorialize the life it had once sheltered. It must have started quietly turning back to dust the moment my father's dying body was carried out.

Its forlorn shrunken silence drowned the top twenty and the commercials, even at a distance. In the end I found I could not go nearer. I am not fond of the condition of tourist, yet I can bear to be one in other corners of the world. But not there—I couldn't bear to be a tourist there.

So it was that, of all the scenes of childhood which held great significance for me, I saw only the one which was clearly visible from the road over which I passed and repassed. But this scene held no memories of hay-fields or berry picking or walks for pleasure.

It was a long bald hogsback of a hill. The top had never been scarred by the plough, being strewn with boulders and its topsoil visibly eroded. During the drought the top was brown and blistered early in the year. Around the boulders were clusters of ant-hills, and an intricate and permanent pattern of their runs ran from colony to colony, and must have been many hundreds of yards long in all. The hogsback lay on Ed Brown's land, astride my footpath across the fields to school.

Sometimes I lingered uneasily to contemplate the ants and their works. Sometimes I fled across their empire as fast as my scrawny legs and the apparently inevitable stitch in my side would let me, for ants were first among my personal symbols of menace at the time: I seemed hardly to pick up a book without identifying with some African missionary or explorer contriving to get himself tied up near an ant-hill to be stripped, molecule by molecule, to the shining white bone. But it was not the ants which finally wedged that hill into my memory.

One day an impending dust storm made the teacher dismiss us early, with a parting 'Run all the way home, all of you!' We couldn't quite do that of course. I had only a couple of miles to go, but there were some with three or four. But we understood the message all right. Indeed it was superfluous. Dust storms were fearsome and dramatic. They approached in great indigo clouds boiling with sinister coppery advance masses. Their sound was as of the approach of a herd of panicking hoofed animals. They came on swiftly, for only strong winds could lift and sustain the dense clouds.

I still had about a mile to go, having just crawled through the fence off the road and run down into the hollow from which the hogsback rose, when the cloud at my back lost its indigo velvet appearance and revealed itself to be a thick dirty grey. Light and colour drained abruptly from the near landscape, as at an eclipse of the sun. The first bits of dried straw and leaves, the first wisps of fine dust, were just being plucked from the ground around me. I was gasping for breath and determined that whatever happened I should get over the long, exposed hill before the thick of the storm should envelop me, when I was suddenly stopped dead in my tracks. Three coyotes, dog, bitch and pup, appeared on the path before me, right at the crest of the hill. Normally this would have been a pleasing excitement. They are timid animals, and one is seldom privileged to have a good leisurely look at them in the wild. But this time they too seemed engrossed in the oncoming storm, and ignored me. I took a few steps towards them but they didn't move. I shouted—it sounded puny to me too, with the roar of the storm just at the nape of my neck. Knowledge deserted me utterly and I conferred upon them magical power to prevent my crossing the long hill to the infinitely desirable shelter of home. I was taking root in silent, dry-eyed hysteria when suddenly the coyotes slipped quietly off: my father had appeared over the crest of the hill, dispatched by my mother to meet me.

In the winter the winds swept the hogsback. For perhaps half a mile there was no shelter. This meant easy walking in that there were no snowdrifts. But oh, the cold! Yet the most memorable winter's day was not especially cold, as I recall.

The teacher had sent me home at lunch time because I was unwell. I was on skis, my cherished first pair of skis, four-foot ones which I had not yet begun to outgrow.

I can't remember how long it took me to get home. Two hours? Three? No one was aware, of course, that it was taking me far too long to get there, as I was not expected home until something past four anyhow. The only part of that journey I could recall afterwards was being down in that same hollow, looking up to the top of the hogsback (a very modest hill really), and just sitting down and whimpering in despair that I should ever reach it. It had looked like the Matterhorn that day. When I did finally reach home, exhausted and doubled up with pain, the nearest neighbour with a car was summoned in haste, and I was bundled off to the hospital in Mafeking, where my appendix was removed as soon as I could be prepared for the operating room.

We needed no awareness of the absolute silence of interstellar space to point up the parable of human vulnerability, the need for some comfort, be it only the animal warmth of other vulnerables. One unremarkable little swelling upon the prairie could work wonders of communication.

Afterwards I couldn't stand the sight of my once-treasured skis. Finally, a horse stepped on one and broke it.

ONCE WE had actually begun our journey to 'down home' my mother exhibited an unwonted diffidence such as used to be common to country folk moving into more sophisticated, unfamiliar worlds. She depended upon me much more than I had expected—indeed she was much more burdened with age and infirmity than I had realized, having seen her only at home where she had arranged things to her tastes and convenience. However, she did not fret and chivvy as she was apt to do in her natural habitat. I saw to bags and tickets, reconnoitred supplies and services, planned and implemented strategies, with scarcely a murmur from her. It was rather heady, being treated by her as an adult of sane mind and rational purpose, and I allowed myself to enjoy it while it should last.

I had hoped we might hire a car and I would have driven us the 1,500 miles each way, but that turned out to be prohibitively expensive—almost twice the train fare for two persons. I was sorry to give up the idea, having always found my mother an excellent passenger in the car, but she soon proved to be equally tolerable by train, being endlessly entertained by any and every passing scene.

Fortunately for our fragile, new-found togetherness, we did not have to travel Canadian Pacific. We did not even have to bother Francis to drive us the extra six miles to Imperia. We had only to go to Regalia, catch the C.N. to Edmonton, change to the C.N. transcontinental to Winnipeg, and from Winnipeg on to St Paul, Chicago and all points in the Middle West it was American trains all the way, and naturally my mother regarded American trains with utter serenity.

I had never before travelled with anyone very old, or incapacitated in any way, or with anyone young and helpless—in short, with anyone who must depend upon the solicitude of those who organize public transport.

I only hope that those responsible for it will spend the last tottering decade of their lives travelling, travelling, endlessly travelling like latter-day Flying Dutchmen over their own transport systems.

The trouble, I decided, was that every other kind of freight was more profitable, was the payload; hence the self-loading freight of humanity had been left to fend for itself. The coaches carrying express packages and mail bags stopped in front of the station waiting-rooms: the passengers walk and walk and endlessly walk to the rear of the train to find an open door which will condescend to admit them; or conversely, to get back to the station when we got off. Temperatures everywhere, now it was mid July, were in the upper eighties if not in the nineties, and even if there was a porter to carry our three bags, by the time my mother had made what haste she could, leaning heavily on her cane on the one side and upon me on the other, we would be winded and perspiring by the time we had reached a destination.

Not that our battles were won merely by reaching the coach. In North America few stations outside the largest cities have built-up platforms extending nearly as far as the monster trains stretch and there are some half-dozen steps built into the train itself, and then one last step which is the conductor's portable mounting-block; there can be a very considerable stretch between this and the lowest step of the train. My mother could no longer climb stairs. Invariably I had to corner the conductor, who would get behind her and lift and heave and push while I (having climbed aboard first and got such anchorage as I could) pulled, mother herself mustering every erg of her failing muscular power. (I had never realized before how heavy she was.) Had the conductors themselves not been consistently good-natured, patient and humorous (nor did they expect tips) this procedure might well have been embarrassing, if not downright humiliating for her. When we had occasion to get on at a small non-terminal station we were invariably warned to be at the ready 'down there' (always a spot disconcertingly near the vanishing point on the horizon) in plenty of time, as the train stopped for only three minutes. At these stops I had always to carry the bags myself, as these stations have no porters, so I would carry the two heaviest down while my mother waited in the shade, then come back for her and the other, and we would toil down and wait, in the blistering broiling sunshine, for the train. If it happened to be fifteen or twenty minutes late that was just too bad for us—we had still to stand there in the sunshine and wait, for there was never shade or seat near enough for anything but a good sprinter to use until the train had actually made its appearance. Then we would bundle ourselves into a coach which might be air-conditioned to something like near-chilly.

Sleeping made a different sort of problem. My mother has never indulged herself in berths or bunks or other special sleeping accommodation when travelling. I had assumed this to be a once-necessary austerity which had just become habit. Approximately the only proviso I had made before setting forth was that we should not spend our nights sitting up in day coaches. I had thought that sort of thing all very well when I was young and the world was just possibly so full of oysters that it was worth going anywhere, under any conditions, to examine the catch. That day is past. I will still go almost anywhere, so long as I can do so in relative comfort. Anyhow, I was paying my own expenses and felt that I had a perfect right to squander my scarce money on beds if I wanted to. Reluctantly my mother had acquiesced. And she didn't object much the first night, when we were in lower berths in the traditional style tourist sleeping-car between Edmonton and Winnipeg. She did grumble a little in the morning, saying that she slept better sitting up, and that she had had some difficulty in lifting herself to a sitting position in the moving train in the night, and in getting out of and into her berth again when the infirmities of old age had obliged her to do so. But this grumble gathered no great momentum. However, the next night, between Winnipeg and St Paul, was a different story. We were obliged then to settle for one of those goddam exercises in engineering ingenuity, as nothing less elaborate was provided on the line. This one was in the shape of a little self-contained metal cage which, except for the padding, was not unlike the cages in which mink and other volatile fur-bearing animals who are inclined to eat their young if disturbed by the sight of others of their own kind are incarcerated for breeding purposes. Cunningly concealed about these claustrophobic cages are wash basin, toilet, bed, table and probably divers other items of furniture which I have forgotten. The look on my mother's face when the porter demonstrated how to pull the bed down! To begin with, one needed to be of more or less normal height to reach the damned thing. My mother is not five feet tall. And then, as you pull the bed towards you, it fences you into an absolutely minimal space—but my mother is minimal only in height, not in girth. I had visions of pulling her out with a corkscrew—popping her like a cork from champagne. Among the items upon which this cunningly concealed bed rested once it had been cunningly pulled down into place was the cunningly concealed toilet. One needed to be either young, energetic and reasonably sober, or else continent, in this place.

I told her that she should ring for the porter to help her should she need to get up during the night, but an idiot could have seen that nothing would have induced her to summon a strange man into her sleeping compartment on any errand

The author—aged four—outside her home

Topsy—not so much a mount as a veritable Earth-Mother of a horse

whatsoever. (Like most women of her time and place my mother was either in bed or else dressed, and had never possessed an ambiguous garment like a dressing-gown.) As the padding on the cell walls precluded her tapping out a summons to me, I said that she should ring for the porter only to ask him to summon me. I would not have been martyred by such a summons, for I am among those who are usually blessed with good sleep, and can easily take it up just where I left off. She was non-committal. In the end she woke up about three in the morning, rang the bell once or twice, but was too diffident to continue ringing when nothing happened, so she struggled out of her bed and finally managed to initiate its heavenward ascent enough to avert catastrophe, but was totally unable to manœuvre it back down and herself into it again. She dressed then, and spent the rest of the night sitting up. The seats in those cages, I might add, were too busy cunningly concealing things to incorporate comfort. They were hard, and the upholstery rasped like an inefficient file at any exposed skin.

I forget how much one pays for the privilege of occupying one of these engineering feats, but I do remember reeling slightly when the figure was named.

The next day my mother said, in a voice so incontrovertible that it would not have occurred to me to offer any debate, that nothing would induce her to subject herself to any more sleeping accommodation on trains. I could do as I liked, she said. There was no reason why I should sit up all night just because she did. But she was not going to lie down, and that was that.

And that *was* that. Subsequently, when we were spending a night on a train, I left my expensive cage to check that she was comfortably installed on her chair in the day coach, then retired to my bed in another part of the train. It is indeed not impossible that I provided onlookers with material for sermons on the degenerate lack of consideration by younger generations towards their elders. . . .

My mother usually managed to look as rested in the morning as I did.

The food problem was usually less complicated when one was actually on wheels than not. Most trains had a restaurant or buffet car, and/or the peripatetic vendor of sandwiches (sometimes

H

delicious), candy, coffee, soft drinks and altogether quite a pedlar's pack of self-indulgence and nourishment. We were not really taken aback until we encountered the city of St Paul. We had a considerable wait between trains there, on our outward journey, and arrived in need of a good breakfast. The station restaurant was permanently closed down. I went scouting and found a restaurant—in other circumstances I should have said 'near' to the station, but it was not very near for my lame, eighty-year-old mother. Nor had the traffic lights where we had to cross to it been set to her gait, and a lot of no doubt normally decent men behind their steering-wheels nearly blasted us out of the street with honking because we did not, when the lights changed, turn into chamois.

On our return journey we had an even longer stop-over in St Paul, as we could not avoid arriving early in the morning and could get no train out until late evening. This time it was Sunday, and even the restaurant where we had eaten before was closed. The station did afford one luxury—a clean, reasonably quiet room where, for a small sum, one could lie down on a clean bed for a few hours, and my mother settled down happily enough to rest for a couple of hours while I went for a walk, in the course of which I assumed that I would find some place to eat. But there was no place. No people. Only a dead, empty, skyscraping city centre, locked up, windy, dusty, undistinguished. I leaned over a wall for a while, looking down on the Mississippi, then went back to the station. We fed ourselves on whatever I managed to find in the slot machines. The sandwiches gave out before noon. We ended up having a supper of potato crisps and other savouries.

On a train in Illinois a woman sat across the aisle from us, thumbing through a considerable pile of magazines. She had brought them from home: I could see the yellow stickers on which the publishers print the customer's name and address for posting. She got off the train before we did. But before she got off she systematically tore off the address labels and dropped them into her handbag. I suppose it was a sensible precaution, lessening the chances of a burglar looking in on her house on the off chance that no one will be in. It wasn't the doing of it that impressed me, but the way in which she did it—furtively, fastidiously, like a cat covering up its excrement. Excessively feline. Which was odd, considering that far from covering up her excrement, as it were, she was leaving it there, strewn all over the seat. . . .

ONCE UPON a time, at a cosmopolitan, sophisticated and largely masculine gathering, I was presented to one— I shall call him Gerry. His principal claim to fame was known to me. He had not long before been honoured during the annual binge and bust-up held at the Correspondents' Club in Tokyo by the presentation of an award—which he was to share with three other American journalists—for having contracted venereal disease more frequently than any other members of the fraternity in that theatre of newsgathering during the twelve preceding months. Gerry was one of the two who actually stepped forth to claim their awards. He was not shy about it at all. But despite the fact that he undoubtedly thought himself interesting and original the reaction he provoked among his peers was perhaps more significant.

During the course of the evening on which I was presented to him, four or five gentlemen, a couple of whom were complete strangers, took me aside for a kindly cautionary word. They didn't want me to be offended—they were not implying anything, or anything—but they had noticed me talking with old Gerry a few minutes ago and they just wondered if I knew that he had V.D. all the time?

The friend who had introduced us overheard one of these cautions and cheerfully corrected it: it wasn't true that Gerry had V.D. *all* the time. If he hadn't had it treated and cleared up regularly how could he have contracted it so often?

Gerry excited in them neither distaste nor censure, and their signals to me were as matter-of-fact and practical as an announcement that a certain bridge had been weakened by recent rainfall, and one should travel by an alternative route if one were going anywhere.

Indeed he provided a sort of touchstone for one sort of liberalism and may (for all I know) have been ripe for canonization by the Burroughs-Genet set, who seem to believe that salvation is to be achieved best by filtering up the sewer pipes and staking a claim on a crack in the enamel of the celestial toilet bowl wherein to lodge eternally. The acquaintances I shared with Gerry were not in the canonization trade, however; their speciality was broad-mindedness, torrents and torrents of indulgent broad-mindedness—something like the St Lawrence River in full spate.

Which is just dandy, of course. But I suspect their broad-mindedness of being very selective indeed. Now, if my Aunt Minnie had walked in on that same sophisticated cosmopolitan and largely masculine gathering, I am pretty sure that that torrent of indulgence would have dwindled to the merest trickle in a very short time. For Aunt Minnie was unmistakably an Old Maid, the very pattern from which Old Maidenness was cut. Her presence in that gathering would have reminded practically everyone (except, possibly, Gerry himself) that his sobriety left something to be desired, perhaps, that his boy scout badges were fraying around the edges. Each would have blamed her because his estimate of himself was diminished even though she would have been too shy, too pacific—and probably too uncomprehending— to have uttered any criticism of them at all. They would have rationalized their resentment, perhaps, brought out that boring old cliché about Old Maids being anti-Life. But when I think of the life-shatterers I have known, there is not one Old Maid in the lot.

Now, in *Cranford*, Aunt Minnie would have been quite unexceptionable. She was the nearest thing to Miss Matilda Jenkyns that I shall ever know. We were to stop over with her for a few days before going on to the little town where Uncle Frank lay dying.

Aunt Minnie's independent career had started, like my mother's, with school-teaching. As she was quite deaf, following upon the scarlet fever from which she nearly died in infancy, it seems a brave choice of profession. But she ever loved children, and triumphantly survived a couple of decades of teaching. Then somewhere in the mid twenties her brother Estley's wife died, and Aunt Minnie dutifully gave up her career and went to live on his bleak, comfortless farm in the middle of the treeless Saskatchewan prairie to mother his three little children and keep house.

This she did for a few years until Uncle Estley married again, at which time of course the spinster aunt was expected to quit her unpaid post, pack up and leave, with no home to go to and the parting handshake far from golden. She was also expected to give up the children who had become to her as her own, her principal pride and joy, the centre of all her tender affections. She was expected to do all this in a quiet, seemly fashion.

However, it must have been almost simultaneously that her brother Bernard's wife died. Uncle Bernard too lived on a farm— a more organized, efficient, comfortable farm—only a few miles from Uncle Estley. Uncle Bernard too was left with young children: four of them. Aunt Minnie dutifully moved in and mothered them. She must have been with that brood for about ten years, and seen the youngest of those children sixteen or seventeen years old, when Uncle Bernard decided to remarry.

By now Aunt Minnie had lost her professional standing as a school-teacher, standards, curricula, educational methods and philosophy having altered so drastically between the early twenties and the late thirties. She was understandably upset and embittered by this blow. Uncle Bernard, who was a rather nice soul himself, had a bad conscience about it, and his children were up in arms against the alliance which threw this gentle, decorous, timid lady out into the world to fend for herself at the age of about fifty. But love will find a way, and thrown out she was.

After this she had returned to Iowa to be housekeeper in a succession of households, mostly consisting of aged near-invalids. At the time of our visit she was housekeeper to a woman doctor, pillar of her community and her church, of the Women's Missionary Society and, until her recent retirement, of her profession. My mother had started, early on in our travels, to sing the praises of Dr Baron; and sing them and sing them and sing them until I soon suspected the worst. My mother's taste in people is not inclined to coincide with mine.

Simultaneously my mother was conspicuously *not* singing the praises of my Aunt Minnie. They had always been oil and water, those two. At the moment they seemed to be at loggerheads as well, if oil and water can engage in loggerheads.

Aunt Minnie had it seems been informed of our impending visit, and far from inviting us to come and stay with her had suggested emphatically that we should stay in an hotel. Personally I sympathized with Aunt Minnie, and would have much preferred to oblige her. I tried to persuade my mother that we were an imposition, that Aunt Minnie was after all only an employee of the remarkable Dr Baron, and that even in a reasonably egalitarian society it is not common for an employee to billet visiting relations on her employer. I did not mention that the prospect of a few days in the house of such a paragon as this Dr Baron filled me with some alarm, but it did. My mother didn't even try to reason with me. She simply stated that when I met Dr Baron I would realize how irrelevant my theories were—and how cantankerous Minnie was being. She said that Dr Baron would be downright offended if we harboured any doubts of her hospitality. To my mother hospitality towards strangers is as inviolable as if Zeus still reigned. To her credit, she has not noticed that it is not necessarily so with others. She herself was shocked by Aunt Minnie's attitude, which violated such a deeply ingrained code.

When we arrived at the town I tried to telephone Dr Baron's house from the station, but got no reply. My mother was adamant; she would not do Dr Baron the injustice of checking in at an hotel. She wouldn't even let me put our suitcases into the left-luggage at the station, which I felt would have been more tactful, giving our hostess an opening to assume that we had just dropped in, in passing, without meaning to pitch our tents. I had to resign myself. This was my mother's trip, this her country, these were her friends. Anyhow, I muttered to myself as I loaded us, bags and all, into a taxi, them as labour to create an image of themselves as paragons ought to have to labour to sustain it now and again.

It was our arrival at the Baronial mansion that convinced me that I ought, for the first time in my life, to keep a journal. Here truly was deepest America, not marked for export, untrodden by any but the most intrepid foreign explorer, of whom none apparently has lived to tell the tale, or at least to publish it.

The house was a substantial white frame house in a quiet residential street of largish old-fashioned houses not yet starting to run down, but almost certainly due to commence that sad process fairly soon. There were a lot of fine elms and, for all the heat, an impression of shade, and the air stirring enough to take the punch out of the heat. We were greeted at the door by Aunt Minnie and Dr Baron, both of whom had just arrived home from their separate excursions.

It was probably more than twenty years since I had seen Aunt Minnie. She had visited us once when I was too young to remember anything more than that she had been—probably that was when she was between uncles, as it were. Then she had spent a month or six weeks with us when Uncle Bernard married. I would have been fourteen or fifteen then. Although I had not been able to conjure up her image before the door opened, the moment I saw her I could remember that this was exactly how she had been; strikingly symmetrical hair parted dead centre, clothing cut with matching, never contrasting, sides. Although she was of course not wearing a hat, it was instantly obvious that she was a wearer of hats, that they would all be set dead centre and anchored to her bun, and that their axes (plural of axis, not chopper) would be horizontal, not perpendicular. Only the silk cord which secured her pince-nez had no mate, but it radiated no rakishness. Although she was moderately plumpish she looked somehow fragile. I think that was her colouring, the delicate pink of her cheeks and the pastel colours of her clothes. Feminine. Quite remarkably feminine, to associate with voiles, muslims, dimity, perhaps even chiffon. My mother looked female to her feminine; Dr Baron neither feminine nor female, but husked like some social insect born to work, not to reproduce its kind—like a worker wasp. Aunt Minnie offered me her cheek to kiss and it was unbelievably peach-soft.

She tried to look welcoming, but obviously she was affronted and wished us in Kingdom Come. She tried to find something warm and welcoming to say to me, for she knew intuitively that it was not I who had wished this descent upon her head. She looked at me, trying to find something about me to trigger a welcome, but her eyes fled from my varnished toenails peekabooing through the flat Italian sandals, to my stockingless legs (when the temperature is over ninety in the shade, nylons are quite simply unbearable), to my varnished fingernails, to my lipstick and blonde hair, and sighed. 'You *do* take after your father so,' she said. Then hastily, lest she be thought critical, 'I didn't mean it as a criticism. Just a fact. There is just nothing of our family in you.'

I bore the deprivation with fortitude.

Dr Baron compensated for Aunt Minnie's lack of effusion. No doubt about it, my mother had been quite right. She *was* pleased to have us stay with her. Our coming had sent the requisite shudder through her web and out she pounced.

My mother presented her to me solemnly, as though we were in the presence of a magnificent natural phenomenon or a unique artistic masterpiece. Me she served up to Dr Baron in the shattering, unprecedented form which, it turned out, was to be mine for the duration.

'And what do you think of My Baby?' she asked Dr Baron. I never did come to a decision as to which was preferable—to look casual, or to pretend I was actually somewhere else.

Dr Baron inquired after my name.

'Heather Gilead,' I said.

'Heather,' she said, brushing off the possibility that I might have a surname. 'Well, Heather, everyone calls me Dr Belle. You will call me Dr Belle and I will call you Heather.'

We set about the business of Making Ourselves at Home. Indeed my mother *was* at home. I have never seen anything like it, and it was not without poignancy. The doctor's house was spacious, correct, impeccable, comfortable even. Nothing ultra modern. It had no graces. Pictures and bric-à-brac, which might have brought the middling good furniture and curtains into line, brought instead the stale odour of air-conditioned department store 'galleries'. Comfort and decency were necessities, but aesthetics suspect. But it was a much better house than anything my mother had ever had, or could have aspired to even in her moments of extreme optimism on those prairies where so large a fraction of all effort went into just keeping warm seven months of the year. However briefly, my mother simply appropriated this house, revelled in it, assuming a formality and gentility of which I had indeed seen flickerings upon occasion, but which I had never before seen effortlessly sustained. As the days went by in that house I became more and more convinced that given easier circumstances my mother would probably have been infinitely easier to live with; that the thorns and jagged edges with which she seemed to have become afflicted over the years were largely barnacle growths—foreign bodies settled upon her from the environment, rather than emanations from herself. She did not appear to pay much attention to what went on around her in the house. She just settled herself somewhere, passive and beatific, radiating a contentment which was pathetic by its rarity.

My own joy was somewhat less unconfined. We had not been half an hour in that house before Belle Baron had set up an occasion upon which to disclose that during her years of medical practice she had usually had an Unfortunate Girl as housekeeper— and how grateful many of them had been, and how they sent Christmas cards and all. She sounded as if the supply had been pretty adequate. Now that she had retired she had taken in Aunt Minnie. She said this as if Aunt Minnie were another of her charities. She esteemed Aunt Minnie very, very highly, she said with some severity, assuming that I was too dim to recognize Aunt Minnie's qualities. As Aunt Minnie was not as robust as she had once been (she was, after all, seventy-five), she, Dr Belle, magnanimously hired a daily woman to help with all the really heavy work. I reckoned to myself that Aunt Minnie was probably still worth her weight in gold and that plenty of people would have felt thankful, rather than charitable, to have her managing their kitchen, shopping, linens, the general organization of the household and generally relieving them of all the minute, tiring, time-consuming responsibilities of daily life. It was Aunt Minnie who kept that house looking not only lived in but loved and caressed. You can't tell me that the shine on that furniture was entirely due to the efforts of the daily cleaning woman; the minute her back was turned Aunt Minnie would have repolished the whole lot.

'Minnie will have a good home here until she dies,' said Dr Belle, lest any of her luminosity be obscured by a bushel. But I had to admit to myself that this was a good thing from Aunt Minnie's point of view. She too obviously felt happy in this house and this company. Well, it takes all kinds.

Dr Belle confided too that her fondness for Aunt M.—and the fondness was genuine, I am sure—made it a pleasure to oblige her in the matter of putting us up for a few days. While she was telling me this Aunt Minnie was charging about her kitchen like a fragile, ancient thundercloud, humiliated and angry with us for being there; and with Dr Belle in the parlour, congratulating herself on rejoicing the venerable auntly heart.

It was just about at this point that I slipped out to the kitchen to inquire of Aunt Minnie if she could produce an ash-tray. It was the last straw! As if she knew for a certainty that it carried plague she extracted, from the back of a bottom cupboard, an old scallop shell. She looked as though I were about to shame her utterly in full view of all whom she held dear. I inquired if I ought to do my smoking outside on the porch. She thought that that would not be necessary—but if I did so would I confine myself to sitting on the *back* porch where I would not be visible to all passers by and neighbours. Dr Baron had always insisted on the necessity for responsible persons to Set Examples at all times. It would not be a very good thing to see people smoking on a doctor's veranda.

And upstairs, downstairs and in my lady's chamber, wherever I encountered my mother, she said, 'Don't you think Dr Baron is wonderful/swell/dandy/nice?'

I invariably said yes.

SINCE RETIRING from practice Dr Baron had been able to indulge many of the desires she had long cherished but been unable to find time for. Especially she had taken to travel, visiting missions in Darkest Africa and India. My mother had promised me that we should have a lot in common, the doctor and I, since we had both done some travelling.

It so happened that our sojourn in her household coincided with the visit of Patrice Lumumba to the United Nations in New York. The front pages of the Chicago papers were almost exclusively preoccupied with the Congo—I had been noticing with fascination how, in this erstwhile stronghold of isolation, the fourth estate was now energetically disseminating the information that the 'natives' (of Cuba, Darkest A., etc.) were 'unready for complete responsibility', were 'politically backward', 'immature', etc. They did all but summon up the white man's burden in so many words.

Anyhow, since Dr Baron had recently visited the Congo, I thought I might venture it as a topic of conversation. And so, when conversation time rolled along, I asked her what she had thought of the Congo during her recent visit.

'No roads,' she said firmly. 'There are no roads along the Congo River. None at all. It's not much like the Mississippi.'

There was that in her manner which declared the subject to have been dealt with exhaustively.

However, she can apparently find something to say when the spirit moves her. While she is on her travels she keeps journals which she subsequently edits into circular letters. My mother had been fortunate enough to get a copy of one and had read it out to the Ladies' Aid. They had voted unanimously to the effect that it was very, very interesting.

My mother told Dr Baron that I had been living in London and Paris. I don't know why she should have thought this would impress Dr B. It doesn't impress *her*, after all. Dr B. urged me to tell *all* about it. I settled for a brief account of the uncanny promptness with which all imperishable foodstuffs—rice, flour, pastas, spices, tea, coffee, oil, etc.—had simply disappeared from the shops of Paris in thirty-six hours at the time of the Hungarian revolt when everyone assumed that World War III was on the doorstep. Thus I had realized, in the face of such an automatic and unanimous reflex action, how sheltered and secure our own existences were. Those foodstuffs had disappeared before I had wakened to the fact that one ought to concentrate some attention on them.

'How very interesting,' said Dr Belle. 'Isn't that interesting?' she appealed, as chairman, to the other ladies who composed the meeting. Aunt Minnie, who had probably only half heard me—my voice seems to lack penetration, and deaf persons find me particularly difficult to hear—agreed that it was very, very interesting. My mother looked benevolently gratified, as if her baby had succeeded in saying 'Little Bo-peep' right through without a single mistake. Dr Baron then changed the subject; we had had Europe, and the meeting was adjourned.

Television was strictly rationed in that household to informational or uplifting items. We concluded our first evening's entertainment with a lengthy programme, direct, of the closing session of the Democratic nominating convention. Even on the small screen the pitch of excitement, the pull of the whoop-de-doo, came over. What was actually being said was as usual of no moment, except as faint garbled intimations of the cross-currents of energy, purpose and confusion beneath. The very absurdity of the hats and balloons and bands and cheering, the very hollowness of the words spoken by men as if they had that power and omniscience which the historian will almost certainly deny them, are moving. Here, one may feel, is collective man casting his bread upon the waters in a great act of faith which he pretends is a great assertion of knowledge.

The television was switched off at ten-thirty, and the household was packed up for the night. Unaccustomed as I am to sleeping at that hour—to say nothing of that heat—I would have been happy to sit up reading, or making notes for my journal, for a couple of hours. But when Dr Belle packs up a household it is packed up. And as I was obliged to intrude yet again on Aunt Minnie, who had to share her bed with me, there could be no question of self-indulgent reading upstairs.

It was much too early to sleep. I might have enjoyed a good threshing about in the hot, humid night, but felt obliged to lie carefully, on the very edge of the bed, not twitching a muscle, waiting for her regular breathing to tell me she was asleep. It was a long wait. I meditated upon my situation. It was comic enough, given its ephemeral nature and the fact that I was a volunteer and could be coerced only with my own consent. But how horrifying it would have been to be permanently imprisoned by such a trio! How I should have hated to be young and vulnerable in that house—perhaps in that society, even.

118

La Belle Baron walked like one accustomed to obedience—a latter-day variation on the theme of the man on horseback. Was Iowa littered with citizens ready and waiting to obey—or concur?

The next morning I declared my intention of walking about town, looking for the local sights. Dr Belle immediately invited herself to accompany me, perhaps out of hospitality, perhaps out of a desire to instruct, or perhaps out of a reluctance to allow me to run about without supervision—or some combination of the three. Understandably, there was little just loafing about looking at things, or absorbing atmosphere. The more edifying sights were laid on for my entertainment, principally the campus of the local college, the Christian nature of which was emphasized several times. It looked pleasant enough, with spacious grounds and buildings, but it was closed for the long vacation, except for the swimming-pool and gymnasium, which were available to worthy youth groups during the summer.

During the course of our walk we encountered several citizens, all of them apparently prosperous and all acquainted with Dr Baron. I was introduced, if at all, as 'Minnie's niece from England'. Apparently I had no name. Although she did not chat for more than a few minutes with any of them, anti-Catholicism raised its head perhaps two or three times in the course of seven or eight encounters. It seemed exceedingly zealous to me, to be that Protestant before lunch, and with the temperature already into the nineties, but of course a Catholic had emerged as Democratic candidate for the White House the night before and it was all hands to the pumps to avert foundering in the threatened tide of papal corruption. There paraded again my venerable acquaintances—the hints of lurid sexual goings-on in monastery and convent. There was the indignation against politicking priests who shepherd their obedient baa-lambs to the polls. One woman claimed that the Catholic Church deliberately kept its people poor. Not without malice I threw in my five-cents' worth, of how the French Canadian Catholic Archbishop in Montreal had, during my time there, campaigned vigorously against not only godless communism, but also against socialism, on the specific grounds that they aim at the elimination of poverty, whereas Christ had laid down that we were to have the poor always with us. The ladies started to toss in the odd crumb of approval before they realized that they could not be comfortably anti-Catholic on that basis without seeming to suspect some goodness in socialism or communism. I was given an opportunity to clarify my own position, but chose to see no necessity to do so. In the end, after a little fumbling, they managed to get my contribution to the debate wrapped decently in a bit of old newspaper and carried at arm's length to the nearest garbage can. From that moment, I was gratified to observe, Dr Baron knew that all was not right with me. She treated me with a certain asperity, the hint of a cutting edge. The word 'matoority' started cropping up pointedly in her talk. I gathered that people who hold wrong opinions are psychologically, politically and/or socially 'immatoor', and that this is lamentable. She almost started seeing me, I believe, as a separate independent person.

Aunt Minnie soon forgave my mother and me for coming. I had not disturbed her sleep the night before as she had been so sure I would, although she told me that she had wakened at four in the morning and lay awake for a long time, trying to solve our problems—my mother's problems and mine, that is. I told her that, so far as I knew, I had no 4 p.m. problems, let alone 4 a.m. She apologized disarmingly, and indicated that a chronic worrier like herself sometimes just runs out of agonies of her own and has to borrow a few to see her through the small hours. She was embarrassed now for yesterday's chilly reception. I found myself, to my amusement and dismay, smoking only half my usual quota of cigarettes, and those furtively on the back porch, not because I feared her displeasure but because my smoking seemed genuinely to grieve and alarm her.

I was even allowed to wipe dishes, although I could see that she had no great confidence in my ability to do it properly. Dishwashing was a most precise ritual with Aunt Minnie. Having collected the dirty dishes at the banks of the Jordan, as it were, she:

(a) scraped all messy surfaces thoroughly with a rubber scraper;
(b) wiped any recalcitrant mess—grease or egg—with a paper towel;
(c) rinsed each dish under the cold water tap;

(*d*) rinsed each dish under the hot water tap;
(*e*) scrubbed diligently in hot water with liquid detergent;
(*f*) soused in hot soapless water;
(*g*) baptized in boiling water;
(*h*) wiped, or suffered to be wiped.

However, one advantage of this ritual was that it allowed for leisurely chat. I inquired if she did not find my mother's total recall of her youthful life in Iowa touching. As I suspected she had rather found it an irritant. During my mother's previous visit to the States (which it is quite possible my mother had privately thought might well be her last, and which she had made in the company of my already senile father), she had invited herself and husband to visit—and frequently to make quite extensive sojourns in the homes of—divers persons whom my mother recalled very well, and affectionately, but who scarcely remembered her and cared less. Admittedly, these visits would hardly have been memorable for their jollity. My father had had to be kept under surveillance all the time, for he lost his bearings completely in the strange surroundings. My mother had already told me of the nightmare of allowing him to go into public lavatories when travelling. Eventually the inevitable happened; he left one through an entrance opposite to the side of the building on which she was waiting for him and drifted aimlessly about the streets, with no clear recollection of what city he was in or why he might be there, and she spent a frantic hour until the police finally located him for her. Typically, my mother's reaction had been cross; she had warned him about leaving through the wrong door, but he wouldn't pay any attention to her. . . . Aunt Minnie had frankly found her ancient sister an embarrassment, and wished she would stay at home or else learn not to impose on people.

I reminded Aunt Minnie of the hard, comfortless, often unduly solitary life my mother had had. Aunt Minnie looked a little surprised at first. It may never have occurred to her, in her unmarried state, that there is precious little companionship in a bookworm, regardless of the vows, or that the latter years of my father's senility might have been far more claustrophobic and isolated than her own busy urban existence. When she visited our home she may well have neglected to notice how much of the defective housekeeping and sanitation was due to circumstances beyond my mother's control. So used was she, from away back, to being on the defensive against her formidable sister that she had never thought of her, of all people, as being vulnerable.

Typically, however, she rejoiced to find a good reason for feeling more magnanimous towards my mother, and she started doing a little penance for having taken seriously what had amounted, at worst, to a little social insensitivity on my mother's part. And it was with some gaiety that she said that she would have to find a whole new set of worries if she left off worrying about what people were going to think of my mother, but she thought that some alternative would present itself.

Although she had come to quite like me, alien though I was, she had also noticed that I had been able to contain my enthusiasm for her idol, La Belle Baron. The possibility that anyone might not be instantly devoted to Dr Baron filled her less with resentment than with incredulity. So great was her disbelief that I could only suppose that, in all the decade or so she had spent in that house, no one who was immune to that lady's charms had darkened that door.

Frankly, it turned my bowels to witness my mother's grateful acquiescence in the doctor's patronizing, which she mistook for genuine courtesy—and her mistake did her credit. Dr Baron invariably spoke to her a little loudly, in very simple language, although my mother was not at all deaf, nor was her vocabulary necessarily inferior to the Baronial one. Dr Baron fussed over her as if she were much further sunk in decrepitude than she really was. I didn't begrudge my mother a bit of attention— she's had no surfeit of it—but just the character of it. There was its ostentatious righteousness to begin with. Dr Baron couldn't bear to see me quietly reading my book for a few minutes, for instance, so she would march in briskly to plump a cushion at my mother's back and shoot me a see-how-much-more-attentive-to-the-geriatrics-I-am-than-you-are look. And I wanted to scream, 'Don't you dare try to push her into the geriatrics yet. She's not finished. She's no more finished than you are!'

So my mother's undying gratitude for that damned plumped

Mother and her siblings. *Standing, left to right:* Mother, Aunt Minnie, Aunt June.
Seated: Uncle Frank, two Saskatchewan uncles, Uncle Ray

Father and Mother   Aunt Minnie

pillow—which had not even increased her comfort—was almost unendurable.

When Dr Baron inquired whether I went to church in London I answered, 'No'. Upon which she decided, on her own initiative, that I wasn't 'a regular church member'.

The oppressiveness of the house lifted considerably, however, after the Saturday evening when Dr Baron went out to keep a dinner engagement, leaving us to fend for ourselves. Aunt Minnie invited Leona, a friend of my mother's youth, to have supper with us. It was pretty clear to me that in arranging this dinner Aunt Minnie was exercising her liberalism to its limit.

There are few persons in whose company one can spend several hours without finding something attractive or at least worthy of notice about them. Even Dr Baron, for instance, was always trim in her well-cut dresses. Little as I liked her I suspected that she might, in some circumstances at least, have been a very good medical doctor. It was easy to imagine her sitting hour after hour, attentive and competent, neither bored nor impatient, giving Death a real run for his money, shaking him off if he was to be shaken off.

Leona, however, disclosed nothing which dimmed her unloveliness in my eyes. At this present distance of time I can recall nothing of Leona except that she was a sort of passive, sluggish chunk who seemed oddly enough to provide the perfect foil for a streak of unsuspected vivacity in my mother. The note I wrote concerning her the morning after, however, informs me that she was seventy-eight years old, stolid, solid, her mousey-to-white hair frizzy with an uncared-for perm.

In anticipation of her visit my mother changed into her third dress. We were travelling very light; my mother had brought only three dresses, of which two were discretion itself, one lavender, one a honey colour. The third had to be seen to be believed, however—especially on a small, pear-shaped, white-haired octogenarian. On a black jersey background was set a riot of the most abominable roses ever imprinted upon fabric: electric pinks and reds, screaming yellow and bilious clutching greenery. My mother has always had a tendency to schizophrenia in clothes, most of them being so sufficiently appropriate that the remainder are incredible. The wardrobe she was carrying was an

I

almost perfect example of this divided self. And on that Saturday evening, in the company of Leona, I believe I witnessed at long last the woman who lay behind the flamboyant atrocities.

To begin with, their talk, which was unfailingly cheerful—almost ghoulishly cheerful in the circumstances—was of those common acquaintances who had died or at the very least been widowed. This was intermixed with some trifles of shared ancient history which (as usual) my mother recalled as if it were only yesterday. Then they moved casually on to a truly Euripidean tale of the woman of their acquaintance who had broken up her daughter's marriage, pursued the son-in-law (eighteen years her junior) to California, upon which he fled to Mexico. She tried to follow him but was stopped at the border by the authorities. In the end she got him though, and married him herself. In speaking of all this they used the language proper to outrage: 'What kind of woman . . . ! What sort of man . . . ! Terrible! A scandal!' But they were not scandalized, nor even particularly titillated. Aunt Minnie appeared to have switched off her hearing-aid. They paid no attention to her or to me.

Indeed, as if they were still giggling girls exchanging intimacies in strictest confidence, my mother spoke of a man with whom they were mutually acquainted, and with whom she had been exchanging Christmas cards for fifty years. His very name excited such hilarity that he must once have been a community joke. He had, I gathered, spoken with a funny foreign accent—Swedish, or maybe German—and had always wanted girl friends like other normal men, but had never succeeded in getting himself taken seriously by any eligible girl. He had never married. But when he had heard of my father's death he had sent my mother a postcard—she had thought the picture on it very pretty, it being of ostriches at the local zoo—inviting her to come to visit him at his expense. He would put her up in the very best hotel in town and all. Both the ladies considered this tantamount to a proposal of marriage, and gave vent to some rather un-grandmotherly—or, in my mother's case, un-great-grandmotherly—giggling. The joke, it was made plain, lay in the pretensions of the suitor; my mother obviously still felt herself to be eligible.

Aunt Minnie's hearing-aid must have been turned on after all, for she began to look distinctly uncomfortable. She looked hopefully at me once, wondering if I would come to her aid, but nothing would have induced me to cloud this minor revelation. I wore my best Impassive Neutral Observer face and kept quiet. Laughter rattled the teacups. Every rose on my mother's third dress doubled up with mirth, whooped with delight. There could have been no question that either the lavender or the honey-coloured dress could have taken the measure of this situation. A *soupçon* of the rank mafia presence of the goat god pervaded the house insolently as it might never have done when Dr Belle was there, even if her house had swarmed with swollen Unfortunate Girls. You could see the alarm rising like a tide in Aunt Minnie. She attempted with polite fluster to change the subject, but they laughed at her rudely, as sexually knowledge-able and unrepentant persons laugh at spinsters, and briefly entertained themselves by deliberately shocking her. (And in front of 'the baby' too!) You could see that she had thought herself quite secure in the doctor's house, with its order and lack of surprises, with her pastels and symmetry, and the restraint with which the vinegar had been added to the boiled salad dressing, and old age. It was shattering to find that even all this was not enough.

By the way they spoke to her I could tell that this too was just a postscript to an ancient comedy, to which Aunt Minnie had unwisely written *finis* a few decades too soon. For myself I could plainly see that the image of my mother I had been accumulating and packing about with me for thirty-eight years would have to be touched up a little. It could never be quite the same again.

The next day was Sunday. Without asking, I was excused from accompanying the three worthies to morning service. In the afternoon I accompanied them, meekly enough, to a service in the local Negro Baptist Church.

The congregation was making its farewell to one preacher and welcoming his successor, and the service went on and on and on. Clearly the congregation did not wish itself elsewhere, and brevity would have seemed small virtue to it. There was a little comfortable coming and going, but mostly people sat relaxed and unfidgety on the numbing wooden seats in the ex-treme heat, the sun pouring in through the windows hour after hour. The choir, to one who is fairly familiar with the spiritual

125

singers who become celebrated, seemed unbelievably lugubrious. They seemed to be competing for the *molto adagio* prize, and also for knowing hymns with the most verses.

The departing preacher, after expressing suitable regret—mingled with a refreshingly plain statement to the effect that there were some in the congregation who would be glad enough to see the back of him—embarked on a rattling good hell-fire sermon delivered with a verve and gusto much enjoyed by the congregation. They followed his form knowingly, like a crowd in the stadium anticipating the more brilliant tactics of their stars. The fires of hell might have been a rip-roaring bonfire to which they flocked to warm themselves and roast their hot dogs. The peaks of eloquence were greeted with shouts of hallelujah or amen, and a sort of fierce gaiety.

When the retiring preacher had finished his sermon—he must have talked for a solid, perspiring, mellifluous hour—his successor's time was not yet come. There were farewell speeches from the lay elders; the presentation of a coat of many colours—a coat which had been passed from family to family, each one sewing on a brightly coloured patch with money and a note of thanks under it; the slow undoing of each patch and public recognition of each gift took a long, gratifying time. This was the sort of thing that we might have done when I was a very young child, when times were reasonably good and sociable and, because travel was primitive, the community was small and fairly close knit. It was astonishing, though, to find it in mid-century urban sophisticated America—and rather touching. A minority thing, no doubt—a ghetto thing—but one which may well haunt the consciousness like a touch of paradise lost as the minority moves out into the limitless indifference of majority.

Just as I was beginning to wonder whether the circulation would ever return to my swollen feet—just supposing we ever did succeed in unsticking ourselves from the seats and walking out—Dr Baron decided that we had done our duty and might depart. Three hours we had sat there, and the new preacher was just embarking on his maiden speech in that house. According to the printed programme, we were about two-thirds of the way through.

We had been the only white persons in the church. Desegregation was, as yet, unself-conscious and unfashionable. Dr Baron had had many patients from that congregation when she practised medicine. Well ahead of any ground swell she had decided that it was her duty to practise a little personal desegregation. The regular congregation seemed neither to mind nor to be impressed. So far as I could see she had not gone to that church for the privilege of worshipping in unison and warm fellowship with the congregation, but out of a sense of duty about as joyous as a dose of castor oil. Desegregation, she had decided, was good for you, therefore she would swallow it.

The next day Alice, a girl of eleven or twelve, daughter of some friend or protégée, came to stay for a few days. Everything —but everything!—served as an example of what she should be or emulate or do. Above all she was to be busy busy busy about infant social work. So assiduously were the shining hours improved upon, so little opportunity had the Devil to catch her with idle hands, that Victoria might still have been Regina. The poor child slipped silently about the house trying to be unobtrusive; she might as well have rung a bell and flashed illuminations. Did she really mind it? I could not have talked to her even if I had wanted to, as she was so constantly chaperoned against evil influences. Dr Baron took her to the movies as a big treat. *Pollyanna*, of course. Dr Baron was most enthusiastic. Alice was polite, but I thought her restraint was the Real McCoy. Dr Baron thought that *we* ought to go, and hardly bothered to disguise the fact that I could do worse than to observe and emulate some improving examples. My mother was enthusiastic about the project, but I decided that it was high time to draw the line somewhere, so I drew it. I offered to escort her to the nearby theatre and to collect her afterwards, but inside I would not go. My mother called it off. She doesn't much care for movies anyhow, and would probably have slept most of the way through it.

Shortly afterwards, in the temporary absence of my mother from the living-room, La Belle Baron delivered a sermon broadside. My mother, she said, was a wonderful, useful person because she was extrovert. Extroversion, she said, is a marvellous quality—perhaps even *the* quality. Because of extroversion my mother had given birth to seven children! Wasn't that wonderful? (If unaided extroversion could do the trick, I thought, it was indeed wonderful. But I kept quiet.)

Aunt Minnie, whose idolatry of La Belle Baron must be perilously close to blasphemous for a Methodist, told me with great preparation and apologies fore and aft that the doctor thought that I smoked too much. She admitted that she thought so too, but would never have dared to mention it had the oracle itself not confirmed it. I told her that I had thought for years that I smoked too much. It was a pity that I did nothing about it, but I thought it unlikely that I ever should. (In fact I did quit a couple of years later—not for any character-building or even hygienic reasons, but simply because the money it costs in Britain is prohibitive. And I don't just miss cigarettes; I feel bereft of them!) I was able to assure Aunt Minnie that the oracle itself had condescended to counsel me directly on the subject. I told her not to lie awake worrying for fear I should be upset by all this discussion, as I bore up well under disapprobation. What *was* an Aunt Minnie to make of that sort of observation? I believe she half expected the house to be struck by lightning or something.

Poor Aunt Minnie! It was not as if my mother did anything to assure the precarious tranquillity of her days. I felt certain that their relationship had not changed since they were little children in their father's house seventy years before, my mother losing no occasion to exercise her authority and seniority, and exasperated by Aunt Minnie's endless scruples and timidities. I remembered being struck by my mother's almost perpetual rudeness to her years before, when she had last visited us in Canada. With a stranger who is a guest in her house my mother is naturally and unfailingly courteous. But with Aunt Minnie it seemed to make no matter what the subject of conversation, or how innocuous it was: Aunt Minnie had had only to venture a fact, or make some deduction from a fact, to have her accuracy or judgment scornfully disputed. This crude knockabout had invariably distressed Aunt Minnie, so that I wondered in the end why she had come. She must have known what would happen. It was still happening.

Our next television feast was the Republican Convention shenanigans. As nearly as one could gather the Country's Choice

lay between Abraham Lincoln and Nikita Krushchev. The preoccupation with Krushchev amounted to an inordinate tribute
to a Russian peasant—even that particular remarkable Russian
peasant. Had he not existed Republican America would surely
have had to invent him.

Eisenhower spoke at some length and said nothing, rather less
intelligibly than most politicians, but cast his spell as surely as
though he spoke with the tongues of angels. It is not credible
that even his worst enemies could deny his absolute integrity,
utter lack of deviousness, his disinterestedness, his humility—
love, even. He must be the only living politician who can preface
his address with the words 'My friends . . .' without either
patronizing or lying.

What a splendid constitutional monarch he would have made,
fulfilling the rituals of state with dignity, ease, selflessness and
charm, making people feel loved, related to, comforted, and
leaving the politicians and legislators to get on with their chores
and intrigues. That a square peg of such spectacular quality
should have been born a citizen of a republic which produces
only the regulation standardized round hole might well be
evidence that there is indeed some Higher Power presiding over
our finite affairs and persons.

After Eisenhower had finished speaking and the hosannahs had
died down a little my mother turned to me and said, with an
unwonted shyness but not without pride, 'I'm a Republican, you
know!' It was the only overt political statement I ever heard her
make, I believe.

Forty-nine years and five months of Canadian citizenship
slipped off like old woollen combinations on the first hot day of
summer! Forty-nine years and five months is a long, long time to
live with your heart somewhere else, even if you don't spend
the whole time grieving, or anything near it.

But however much I might sympathize with her in her
Siberian exile—and life may well not have been all that much
harder for some of those who went, or were sent, to colonize
Siberia—I could not bring myself to wish that she might have
had her heart's desire and lived on in Iowa. Not if it meant
that I would have been born there, in the midst of those suffocating certainties which lay like quicksand on every side.

At the drop of a rosary Dr Baron's anti-Catholicism was upon us. As I had remembered, there was no talk of all those fine points of theology and philosophy upon which theologians write their books. She had strong and rather unsavoury misgivings about that unwed priesthood, to say nothing of all those nuns. The religious community appeared to strike her as the apotheosis of intro-version. She implied that the considerable numbers of Unfortu-nate Girls to be found amongst the flocks of all those celibate shepherds could do with some brisk investigation. But above all her animosity was triggered by the Catholic stand against sterilization and birth control. She herself was an active member of the local committee which decided upon the sterilization of abnormal persons. I tried to question her, being interested to learn whether this sterilization was only voluntary or sometimes involuntary, but she did not answer questions. She was not being evasive; she was simply accustomed to deciding which facts should be disseminated to the public and which were better left in limbo. (I tried once to get her to talk about her early career in medicine. She would have gone to medical school, I suppose, at the turn of the century, which must have made her a pioneer amongst women doctors. Perhaps I had even hoped to catch some fleeting glimpse of a youthful vulnerability which might possibly have been behind the over-compensatory defences which were all that was now visible. But she just looked through me, as a Lord Chief Justice might look through someone who had had the temerity to address a question to him from the dock, and talked of something else.) As she talked about her birth-control/ sterilization work she revealed a truly terrifying certainty that she had the right and the duty to push others around for their own good, and to resolve their indecisions for them. She did not seem to be so much concerned with over-population and the prospect of standing-room-only on the earth, as with the predica-ment of the poor who had 'uneconomic' families. But although birth control seems a rational necessity to me, and an absurd subject to submit to theology, her talk of 'economic' and 'uneconomic' families struck me in the end as obscene. There was this willingness—even eagerness—to intrude upon and mess around with the lives of those who are vulnerable through lack of money. How she seemed to love a limitation—

somebody else's limitation which would deliver them into her keeping.

I gathered (but could not verify) that the law permitted certain categories only to seek legal sterilization: those women who have already had a considerable number of children. Then the abnormals—cretins, mongoloids, persons carrying transmissible abnormalities. . . ? She was too dogmatic to be very informative.

These endless Societies and Committees set up to help the helpless and legislate for the incompetent seem such a good idea at the time—there is always a crying need for them, and undoubtedly they do a lot of essential work. And yet . . . and yet . . . They are irresistible magnets for the Belle Barons of this world. The humble, the scrupulous, those who see all forty-seven sides to every problem, will be elsewhere cultivating their gardens, reproducing themselves, shopping for groceries, playing golf, dusting the piano; or even appearing penitent, embarrassed and bewildered before the Committee. . . .

WHEN DR BARON announced that arrangements had been made to show us through the treasures and pleasures of the city of Des Moines, my mother was in a state of utter beatitude. Sixty-odd years before she had spent a sparkling year here, attending normal school, training to become a teacher.

As we drove through the streets we saw almost nothing which could have been in existence at that time, but this did not seem to diminish her content. Who knows whether the fountains of paradise are eternal, or are eternally changing?

I inquired innocently what monks had given their identity to the city. Getting no reply, I repeated the question, pointing out that 'Des Moines' undoubtedly referred to monks. Had there been some famous mission to the Plains Indians? Or some celebrated early seat of monastic learning?

It was the very first time I had stopped to count it out. One, two, three, four. Yes, there was no doubt about it—monk is a four-letter word. I still do not know what monks are celebrated, nor why, by Des Moines, Iowa.

After a brief tour through some of the smarter quarters of the residential section we were required to do the Art Gallery. The building itself was most agreeable, being a model of twentieth-century elegance, by Saarinen, if I remember correctly. Lovely and cool too, with just the right amount of air-conditioning after the heat outside—not the deep freeze that so often passes for air-conditioning. My mother was taken inside and seated (in what was apparently the temporary headquarters of the geriatric ward) while the rest of us—Aunt Minnie, little Alice and myself—were herded smartly to the adjacent celebrated rose gardens. I said 'Oh!' and 'Ah!' in a manner which would (I hoped) seem both convincing and appreciative, but in truth the poor roses were suffering from the heat far more even than I was. The heat dehydrated and hardened the outside petals before the buds fully opened out, leaving the flowers with the disagreeable surfaces of peeling sunburn. The foliage looked limp and rubbery. There seemed no great reason why Iowa should insist upon growing roses. The green and pleasant countryside, with the picturesque cornfields with wild lilies common along the road-side, witnessed to the fact that plenty of things grew handsomely in Iowa. My Uncle Frank, I recalled, had managed to tend an uncommonly pleasant garden in his day only a few miles from here. But I couldn't recall that he had bothered about roses. Dr Baron said that the rose gardens were famous, in a tone which dared us to be unimpressed. By now, guest or no guest, I was quite regularly returning a little rifle fire into her artillery barrages, so I mentioned in my most throwaway manner that in the course of one of her world tours she really *must* take in Kew Gardens. They were not so far from London Airport that she couldn't make the excursion by taxi in the course of a few hours' stopover between flights. So much more restful, I said, than hanging around airports anyhow. . . .

Thence we were herded to the inside of the Gallery, where we were required to expose ourselves to an exhibition of modern French tapestries. We were all lined up before them—my mother, Alice, Aunt Minnie and myself—and I was beginning to take an interest in them, when I suddenly found myself under orders to explain them. Dr Baron sounded a little like my mother when she gets on to the subject of the Canadian Broadcasting Corporation—as if I were somehow responsible for it, and ought to have to provide proper apologetics. It was quite plain that the party was not on the whole much taken (or should I say taken in) by the tapestries. Indeed it seemed a little strange to me that my mother, for instance, who had done a good deal of (admittedly simple) embroidery in her day could not have warmed to them more, but unless the tapestry was dominated by recognizable identifiable objects the reaction ranged from bafflement to something like scorn—all this fuss and publicity for artists who are not even competent to produce recognizable identifiable objects. No one reacted to the magnificent colours or to the craftsmen's skills. It was Art. They had a right to be instructed and uplifted thereby, and I was the chosen vessel.

So far as I know only a handful of persons can speak helpfully on the subject of visual arts, and I am not one of them. I tried. I waded into a pathetic attempt to toss off an instant explanation of modern non-figurative art, but since I don't understand it myself really. . . . If there were any seeds amongst the chaff I produced they fell on to cement. Some of the tapestries were very beautiful, and it was obvious to me from the beginning that anyone who could resist their message would be proof against mine.

I tried a quick, desperate cram of the catalogue notes, thinking they might provide some facts—the number of miles of thread in each work, for instance. I thought that the ladies would like something to take home, and a fact was better than nothing. But the catalogue notes, written by the director of the *Musée des Arts Décoratifs* in Paris (who had mounted the exhibition), were just burble and gush. He hailed something like the coming of the New Jerusalem, which must follow the resuscitation of tapestry weaving. Mankind re-attuned to the music of the spheres. Hand-weaving would be all the craze, the new therapy. I had a wild vision of all the pinball and fruit machines being swept out of Las Vegas to make way for the hand-loom, the Silver Dollar Saloon become the Warped Woof. Hurrah, hurray!

I would have liked to look through the permanent collection of paintings of the Gallery which seemed, as I galloped through, to have an excellent collection of George Grosz, but Aunt Minnie was soon dispatched to round me up.

When we got back from our Des Moines outing Dr Baron handed me a book about the deleterious effects of tobacco. I thanked her for her kind intentions, but declared myself unlikely to profit by them. There was by now a definite thinning of the lips and squaring of the jaw when her eye lit upon me.

At one point she asked me how many children my brother Francis and Marion had. I said ten—which was, in fact, all they had at that time—and she said that they were certainly not practising birth control. I said that this had come to our attention too. With some forbearance I did not ask whether she thought they suffered from an excess of extroversion. She modestly claimed to have done a lot of work among 'the poor', helping them to regulate their families to 'economically possible' numbers. You could tell that she was a woman who loved her work.

During our last evening in Dr Baron's house, in the course of I know not what conversation, I mentioned the old woman with cats who had occupied the basement apartment of the old brown-stone house on West 68th Street in New York at the time when I had for a few months occupied the second floor apartment. New York had seemed to me to squeeze the old and poor into a sort of troglodyte existence, unless they were the—may I say extrovert? —type who can casually expose, and even peddle, their distress around the Bowery. The poor old women one occasionally saw making their furtive little purchases in one of the bulging super-markets of our part of town always looked so unsunned and unaired, so dazzled by the bright lights and dazed by noise, that you did not need to see them do it to know that they darted thankfully into the nearest hole and pulled the lid over, to re-surface only when driven to it by hunger.

I never actually got a good look at the face of the old woman who occupied our basement, but when the hot weather came the stench of her cats—I saw several different ones, at one time or another, lying on the window sill staring out—almost lifted the roof off the building. There was no garden, no patch even of sterile earth near—nothing but stone, pavement, glass. I don't know what arrangement she made for the cats' excrement, but from the stench it was pretty safe to assume that her solution will never find its way into the *Pet Lovers' Manual*. The cats never, of course, went outside, where even the most resourceful must surely have perished within a few hours.

I used to take a deep breath before opening the door in the hot weather, and then try to get to the top of two very long flights of stairs and get my door unlocked, myself safely inside and the door closed, without taking another breath. If I were burdened by great bags of groceries or laundry parcels there was no hope of making it. But sometimes, when I was travelling light, I would manage to make it—a little blue in the face, perhaps, and with a gentle roaring starting in the ears—but still triumphant. Fortunately the stench did not seem to penetrate my apartment to any extent.

Dr Baron said that the poor old woman ought not to have kept cats.

I said that I had not meant to complain. I had merely been making an observation on the phenomenon of solitude, and possibly poverty in old age, as it had fallen under my eye in West 68th Street, New York, during a few months in the summer of 1952. I would have spoken to the woman—at least to say good morning, or nice day, or something—but on the rare occasions when I had been coming down the stairs as she was taking in her considerable quantities of milk she had disappeared hastily, like a startled rodent, as if any intrusion whatsoever was frightening.

Dr Baron said—and she was getting steely again—that the old woman ought to have appealed to the Salvation Army, 'which exists for her sort'.

I did not know what 'sort' she was, and felt myself getting steely right back. I said that perhaps she did not want to be the object of anyone's charity, that perhaps she preferred her independence and her stinking cats, as I would if I were in her shoes.

Dr Baron said that, by my own account, the old woman was

probably 'disgusting'. She whinnied the word with just that *soupçon* of excitement that a sainted medieval leper-licker might have emitted at the sight of an unlicked, divinely suppurating sore.

I made haste to dissociate myself from the word, which I had not used. I did not add that to barricade oneself in the shelter, as if the bombs were falling, looters on the prowl and enemy artillery already battering the suburbs, did not seem to me to be a very incongruous reaction to Manhattan. Although I had felt the excitement of New York when I had lived there I had not managed to accommodate myself to it. My civilian identity, as it were, refused to sink itself into that heady, combatant state without which New York is quite simply appalling. To have admitted that to Dr Baron would have been to confirm her worst suspicions of my 'immatoority'.

Dr Baron said that the Salvation Army could have 'coped with that woman' and that it was her duty—*her duty*—to appeal to them.

After which the only entry I could find to make in my small journal was, 'Glory, Hallelujah!'

I expect Dr Baron was as glad to see the back of us as I was to be shut of her.

Before we retired that night Aunt Minnie entrusted me with a brooch, an old, rather crude silver brooch in the shape of a butterfly, and asked me to deliver it to my sister Lottie. Aunt Minnie had had the brooch from her mother, whose best piece of jewellery it had been, before she died. She wanted to think of it going into the keeping of someone in whom her mother, as she remembered her, seemed to persist. I promised to cherish and deliver it. Poor Aunt Minnie! She then lay awake half the night, apparently, wondering if she hadn't hurt my feelings by not giving the brooch to me.

And that was our last real contact. Since the time when I started to set down these recollections Aunt Minnie, now eighty, underwent a surgical examination, after which they stitched her up again and informed her that she had inoperable cancer. She moved into a nursing home to await her death. The children of her brothers—now grown to middle age or more—journeyed from all over the United States and Canada to offer

136

their love and gratitude while she still lived. My sisters Lottie and Florence managed a flying trip, Lottie's journey being more than two thousand miles each way, to spend three or four days with her. Cousins who had scarcely met and never corresponded suddenly wrote touching little bulletins to one another concerning her state. She faced her slow, agonizing disintegration with knowledge, dignity and, so far as loving eyes could detect, serenity.

It is over now.

MY MOTHER had created a distinct impression of Aunt Flora in my mind: a spare, precise, coolly condescending lady. The woman who met us at the door, however, turned out to be substantial, pleasant, hospitable and, despite the almost dauntingly impeccable house, oddly comfortable.

She thought it best that we should see Uncle Frank one at a time as he could not accommodate two points of interest any more in his failing condition. She led my mother upstairs first and I waited below. Presently my mother came out on the landing. I helped her down the stairs and went up myself.

The bedroom did not reek of death. There was a hospital bed with sides up to prevent my uncle from throwing himself out through the convulsive restlessness of his body. Except for the bed, however, the room seemed a normal conservatively tasteful bedroom with flowers, and curtains stirring at the windows which seemed always to admit a gentle breeze. The room was relatively cool—the coolest room we encountered anywhere, as I recall. Although everything was spotlessly clean there was no commanding smell of disinfectant or medicines.

Uncle Frank had been a solid figure of a man, neither large nor small. He was reduced now to a skeleton. His sunken face was of white wax, his eyes behind their glasses fantastically concentrated, as if he had abandoned the rest of his unruly body to its own devices so that his will might prevail through this one restricted channel.

He took my hot sticky hand in his, which was dry and cold with a cold that made me shiver, and clasped it while he fixed me with his long concentrated stare. He knew that he was soon to die, that his death was already there inside him ignominiously convulsing his limbs and scattering his thoughts like startled chickens. His stare asked nothing for himself, neither pity nor understanding nor even attention.

'How long', he asked, 'since you were here?'

'Ten years. Ten years in September.'

'You're Heather.'

'Yes.'

'You're a very attractive woman.'

No observation could have been more startling, issuing, as it did, from his death's head. Its provenance seemed to invest it with great significance, like the announcements made by ancient fortune-tellers in tragic operas. It seemed to me for days afterwards, until his words faded from my mind, that something must happen to underwrite his verdict, as it were, but not so much as one solitary tree crowded into a shade where'er I passed. . . .

'Your husband was killed,' he continued.

'Yes.'

'I liked him. He impressed me very much.'

'He liked you. You impressed both of us very much.'

'Then afterwards . . . afterwards you went away. Korea. No. No, to the Philippines. I was there once. . . .' His conversation turned confused and unintelligible. He *had* been in the Philippines once. He stared and stared at me, and seemed to be trying desperately to catch the hopelessly lost thread of communication. I could only wait, disconsolate and helpless.

Aunt Flora was briskly practical. 'He'll know you again tomorrow, probably, for a few minutes. Then he wanders. He usually knows people. Then they remind him of something long ago and he goes off.'

She led me downstairs.

My mother had always assumed that Aunt Flora thought herself

138

a cut above her husband's family, and when, ten years before, I had been driving east through blood-relative territory with my husband shortly after our marriage, the prospect of our meeting Aunt Flora had greatly gratified her. The fact that my husband had taught in a university and exuded intellect (and, when he wished, gentility) had seemed eminently satisfactory to my mother. I believe that she had looked forward to throwing the pair of us—but especially John—down before Aunt Flora like a pair of aces with an unspoken challenge to 'beat that!' Alas! We had refused to work out a firm schedule for our itinerary. We would not provide my mother with date and day when our shadows would be darkening the thresholds of relations. We advised her to alert them that some time during the week of —— we would be passing by and would call in. Consequently we had chosen to arrive in this house on an evening when Aunt Flora was away judging gladioli and dahlias in the exhibition of some horticultural society. For years after that my mother sighed over the lack of precision which had prevented our meeting. It would not surprise me, even, to learn that in some unguarded corner of her unconscious mind she was annoyed with John for being killed before Flora could meet him.

Uncle Frank had welcomed us most adequately on that occasion, however. I had not met him before. He was professor of history in the local college—a Methodist college of quite respectable standing. His only published work, so far as I know, was a study written in his youth concerning the nature and influence of Methodism in the Middle West. We had a copy of it at home, and I must confess it was one of the few books in our overstuffed bookcases which I never read. I doubt if Uncle Frank would have minded.

He was of the breed of historians—or teachers of history—who saw his subject as something more than that fragment of the past which has contrived somehow or other to become embalmed between the covers of books. To him history was also a continuous, present and exciting process of which the historian is not only the observer but also a minute portion of the raw material. When we had met him he was, it so happened, more raw than usual.

As I said, Uncle Frank had, about the end of the First World

K

War, been in the Philippines. He had also visited Siberia and Japan at this time, by courtesy and in the uniform of his Uncle Sam if I remember correctly. This was the beginning of a lifelong fascination and curiosity concerning the Far East, its culture and its peoples. Added to this he had, through the Methodist Missions and his college itself, continuing contact with China. Not only had he and his wife been concerned with the encouragement and support of missions and schools in China, but young people of the wealthy Chinese élite had come to be educated in Iowa. His college boasted some celebrated Chinese alumni.

Whether Uncle Frank had personally known Owen Lattimore or not I cannot now remember, but certainly he had been an admiring student of Lattimore's dissertations on the Far East. Thus it was that when Senator McCarthy descended in full blight upon Lattimore, his first substantial victim, Uncle Frank had stuck his neck out. He offered Lattimore a platform by inviting him to lecture at his college. He had assumed that Lattimore's reasoned response would attract something like the attention, publicity and credence the McCarthy denunciations had had. Uncle Frank learned. When we met him he was still reeling—but still game. He had learned that honesty is not enough and that reason is not news. For all the press coverage they got he might as well have done some more weeding in his garden, and Lattimore might have saved his breath and the college its lecture fee. Being a liberal, and a man of principle, it had been painful enough for him to watch the negation of all principle riding in triumph through the land he loved. But being a very human person he had suffered even more through the reaction of his neighbours and friends. His colleagues, fellow church members, neighbours, tradesmen, people he had known and lived among and worked and played with for forty *years*, would ostentatiously cross the street rather than wish him a good morning. Parents were instructing their student offspring to drop courses given by 'that Commie'. He was an outcast in his own street, although he had assured us that there were honourable—and precious—exceptions.

We had talked, the three of us, great guns. We might have known each other all our lives. Aunt Flora had stocked the refrigerator against an invasion of Canadian relatives so that

140

Uncle Frank produced an excellent cold dinner without fuss. We talked through that and through the dishes, talked into the small hours of the morning of anything and everything, solving the problems of the world, charting the cracks in the foundations of liberalism, the precariousness of rationality as a dynamic for social behaviour. I had been impressed among other things at the time with the fact that he was profoundly Christian, so much so that this Christianity was mostly unconscious, and also that this did not grate upon even my husband's agnosticism, which was far more militant than my own. His Christianity was instinctively Protestant. He was a man who could not have sustained the foetal position in a universe which included a possibility of erect and independent posture, a man to nourish his mind and heart from all manner of sources, scorning the cosy placental abundance of a mother church.

He showed us through his pleasant, much-loved little garden and allowed me to cut bunches of grapes. I felt like the priestess in some solemn rite, the significance of which I could not quite formulate. I have never cut grapes since.

All in all, Uncle Frank had not proved to be what my experience of uncles had led me to expect. It was an occasion for rejoicing.

And now I found Aunt Flora equally unlike my experience of aunts. Like her husband had been, she was charming, literate, curious, a good listener and a good talker. My mother presided in benevolent silence over our talk most of the time, when minimal information concerning mutual acquaintances and relations had been dispatched. She said later, when we were alone, 'Say! Flora *can* talk. You and Flora talked just fine.' The chip fell from her shoulder where her sister-in-law was concerned, and was never replaced. She has always understood the difference between an inability to talk one to another, and mere refusal to do so, and she realized now that Aunt Flora, like me, simply could not converse with her at any length.

I was interested in Aunt Flora's Iowa. I had lived with my mother's Iowa, her garden of Eden. I had just lived through Dr Baron's and Aunt Minnie's. I had hopes now of getting closer to what my Iowa might have been, should I have stayed around to stake a claim there. But the differences of generation—Aunt

Flora must have been at least seventy, I suppose, although she looked a vigorous fifty-five—of temperament, of philosophy were too extreme.

She was not dim nor insensitive, would not mistake a tinkle of bone china teacups for Beethoven, but we never really seemed to leave Mary Martin territory, were never more than ninety minutes from that happy ending, music and lyrics by Rogers and Hammerstein.

It was natural enough that she should see her quiet little college town, which furnished goods and services, and gathered in the produce for shipment from the rich rolling farmlands among which it nestled, as a microcosm of America. But although a citizen stopped at random in its streets might well do for Everyman, an agricultural and Methodist college town is not a microcosm of America, nor of the world. Not any more.

She lamented the image of itself which America was sending abroad, the 'decadent' America of Faulkner and Tennessee Williams, whose works she characterized as preoccupied with 'the endless, pointless violence of the second-rate human being'. But her conversation revealed no awareness of even the existence of those thousands upon thousands of rejected human beings for whom the American dream is a nightmare and whose submarine struggles muddy the placid surface waters even if they do not surface themselves. America is vast and various. It is not hard to know less of life in the ghettos of the great conurbations, for instance, than Marie Antoinette knew of the *sans culottes*. Easy not to know about the violences practised or permitted by the accepted in the process of creating rejects and seeing that they stay rejected.

Yet I wondered, after, that the intimations of violence which penetrated to her quiet small-town street were so faint. True, McCarthy was discredited and dead, but only apparently because he had been wrong about the wrong people, not because he had been wrong full stop. The townsfolk who had been so hostile a mere ten years ago had done an about-turn and had dedicated a library to my uncle and aunt by name, in tribute to the faithful services they had rendered to the community. But had Aunt Flora's son Bob brought her no messages from the industrial empires of the eastern seaboard, for instance?

Bob got in touch with me when I was living in New York; he telephoned and asked me to meet him for a drink when I left work. The prospect had pleased me. Uncle Frank could not, I felt, have a son who was a dead loss. It was reassuring that he should have suggested a drink; my Canadian cousins have a tendency to be teetotal, and some of them are missionaries as well. I had visions of the occasional week-end at his home in Boston, of sitting up until all hours of the night nattering of this and that with him and his wife. It was with happy anticipation that I left the office promptly at five and set off to keep our rendezvous.

Doubts set in almost as soon as we had identified one another. Bob, who should have been a tall young man, was merely a long one. He chewed at his lips so consistently and so violently that their outlines had completely disintegrated; his mouth was not much more than a damp bruise, slit horizontally. Before we had finished the first beer he was complaining bitterly of the brutal interruption to his life that the Second World War had been. He had, it seemed, been shipped off to Hawaii without his consent for a period of six months. As this was the nearest he had ever come to shot and shell, dysentery and swampy tropical foxholes, he seemed to me to have done rather better than several millions of our contemporaries. His running on and on about it seemed as excessive as his choice of audience seemed tactless. I was still haemorrhaging internally from the death of my husband in Korea only a few interminable months previously. It was almost unbelievable that an educated, intelligent young man, who would have been in the prime of life had his life had any prime, should be sitting there trying to cadge pity from me simply because he had been obliged to spend six months on Hawaii, passage paid, seven years before.

He invited me to spend that week-end with them in Boston all right, and in due time I prepared myself and set off to endure it. All was as I had foreseen. His wife was suffering from an exasperation which was clearly chronic, but which was temporarily exacerbated by the stifling heat of summer plus eight months' pregnancy. There was a five-year-old boy of the breed which puts the 'infant' in infanticide. The week-end was ghastly. I hammered out a lot of excuses, most of them flimsy, to avoid repetitions,

143

but they were not really necessary. The family was too burdened by its own unhappiness to notice what reception was given to their cursory gestures towards hospitality.

At the time, being short of patience, I wrote them off. Now, in no danger of having to put up with them, with an ocean and several years intervening, I feel softened. Perhaps Bob was— indeed it *seems* to me now that he was—quite simply a quiet, unassuming, pacific, utterly uncompetitive young man who had grown up in a gentle, civilized, uncompetitive home in a musical comedy rural town. He had been so indiscreet as to walk into the barbarously competitive world of the vast industrial complex, a world where, as surely as the guardian of the Golden Bough, he must vanquish all aspirants to his niche or be cast out himself. I shouldn't be surprised if, given half a chance, Bob might not have made a charming and happy cipher, but he was trapped by his advantages. An intelligent, educated, house-broken son of a professor is not allowed to be a cipher. Advantages are his bed of Procrustes, and everyone will have a go at turning the screws to stretch him a bit here, amputate a little more off that bleeding extremity, at pinching and poking and adjusting, until it is small wonder that even a free return trip to a Pacific paradise could come to be a one-way trip into Kafka.

I am sure that Aunt Flora would reject the notion that Bob was being violated. He was not demonstrably a failure as an electronics engineer, whatever his modest success was costing him. He had his decent, if unremarkable, home in a suburb one would not be ashamed to be seen dead in, and had filled it with the inevitable stable of gadgets. And his wife, whose conversation led me to suspect that what she had fallen in love with was not so much Bob as his parents and their ordered, civilized home, was probably at her most gracious and tolerable when Aunt Flora was present.

And even if he could be said to be suffering violence it would presumably be the controlled, wholesome violence of the first-rate.

Well, at least he was in no danger of having a Belle Baron turned loose on him. Now there, I thought, was violence with a vengeance.

WE DID NOT billet ourselves on Aunt Flora. We had settled this in advance. My mother had been disposed to argue the subject, but I wouldn't have it. She was afraid that Aunt Flora would find it offensive on our part not to accept her hospitality—which was indeed offered without any visible reservations whatsoever. But I had checked with Aunt Minnie, who visited the house frequently, and knew that Aunt Flora was on twenty-four hour nursing duty with her helpless, restless, dying husband, that she had been so for months, and that it was an arduous duty. A woman came to help with bathing him and changing his bed in the morning—it needed the two of them to move him—and to give a hand with the cleaning and shopping, but she was there for only three hours, and only during those three hours could Aunt Flora so much as leave the house for fifteen minutes. I could not see that she needed two extra persons for whom to get up and make breakfast, nor could she have needed more sheets to launder, nor be put under any compulsion to be sociable all the day long. I felt reasonably certain that Aunt Flora would adjust easily to our eccentricity if we stayed in an hotel. She did.

Better than I. The hotel was not the worst I have stayed in by a fairly long shot, but it was no picnic. Its amenities were crumbling. Obviously it had once been *the* hotel. I suppose that when Uncle Frank and Aunt Flora had settled down in this town forty years before, the parents of the smart college set might have made this hotel their headquarters when they came to town for the annual graduation ceremonies. Behind some of those glass doors, obscured with dust-filled net curtains, lurked ballrooms and banqueting halls sullen with grubby neglect. One morning the Grand Hotel, conveniently situated in the heart of the town with easy access to the (derelict) railway station, wakened like a flirtatious matron to discover her charming plumpness meta-morphosed into gross obesity, to be treated thereafter to the spectacle of former admirers speeding by on their way to assignations with the motels, snack bars and shopping centres on the outskirts of town. For all the hotel's white elephant size it was claustrophobic. Most of the rooms must have been empty but closed up. There did not seem to be many guests, but the only accommodation they could give us was a double room whose windows looked out into a grimy, airless air-vent. The heat would surely have done credit to Bombay just before the monsoon. The hotel might have drummed up a little trade by putting up a plaque saying that The Salesman's Death Was Inaugurated Here, for surely Willie Loman was discovered by his young son to be shacked up with that excruciating blonde in this very hotel.

I would have been quite happy to lose myself in a book, but I could not concentrate on it at all. My mother did not read, but mumbled and rumbled away interminably like a bee trapped in a bottle, or Arab music. Mostly what she spoke was banal stream-of-consciousness stuff which was not addressed to me, nor on the other hand was it *not* addressed to me. I could neither shut it out nor attend to it for any length of time. Anything and everything would trigger her free associations. She brought out endless caches of railway time-tables from both remote and recent times, interspersed with patient and exhaustive self-interrogation to try to ascertain whether she had arrived at nine or at nine twenty-five, and was that the trip we made when Aunt Lulu broke her arm, or was that when Aunt Hermie invited us to the party. She could do endless permutations and combinations composed of time-tables, neighbours, relations and events, weather reports and fête days from sixty or seventy years back. Although I had rather come to enjoy my mother's reaction to her trip and her old friends and acquaintances, nothing came to our aid when we were alone together. Quite the contrary.

I was already feeling somewhat repelled by what had seemed to me could only be described as a lack of feeling for Uncle Frank. She had seemed briefly touched when she came out of his room the first time, but a few minutes later, when Aunt Flora was talking to me about him and his condition, my mother had repeatedly interrupted our conversation with some comment or inquiry irrelevant to Uncle Frank but which our talk had brought into her wandering mind. She had already 'done' Uncle Frank, I thought, like a tourist 'doing' a museum.

As if to reinforce this impression she was giving me of indifference to the suffering of others, she chose this trap of a hotel room to relive my father's end. It was by no means the first time she had done so in my presence, nor would it be the

146

last. But it did manage to seem more excruciating than usual in this inauspicious setting.

The scene: early spring, four years before. My mother was in the kitchen, over by the stove, overseeing the cooking of the midday meal. My father, who had been sitting in his rocking-chair in the living-room, came out and went to open the kitchen door. She had asked him where he was going.

'Feed the cattle. Got to go and feed the cattle.'

'You haven't got any cattle. The cattle are Francis's now; you haven't got any cattle any more. You go in and sit down now till dinner's ready.'

But he had still persevered, his hands so petrified and crippled with arthritis and time that even the simple turning of a knob had become a major operation.

Her voice, which had already registered irritation when she had spoken to him before, rose in exasperation.

'You can't go out there. There's a blizzard blowing out there. You haven't got any cattle, and there's a regular blizzard. You'd just get lost and the whole neighbourhood'd have to turn out and hunt for you.'

He had continued to mumble something, and fumble at the knob, so she had crossed to the door and flipped the catch, which made the knob impossible to turn. This complication, which she had apparently discovered some time before—the door had never been locked at all, in my time, and there was no key for it anyhow—baffled him completely. He continued to try the knob for some time, insisting on the necessity of getting out and giving vent to some of his frustration and annoyance before turning and shuffling back through the door into the living-room.

She had continued then to get the lunch on the table, and called him when it was ready. He did not make any sign—I believe that this must have been almost the only time during their forty-five years of married life that the prospect of food had failed to rouse him. She went into the living-room, but he was not there. She went into the bedroom and found him collapsed and unconscious, face down, the top part of his body on the bed, his feet and legs sprawled over the floor. She had managed to move him a little, so that his position looked a little less uncomfortable, and then she telephoned to Francis.

It was only here that her voice broke, only here that the pity of it all invariably misted her eyes. Not only was Francis there in less than fifteen minutes, but Harry Brown, who lived a little more than half a mile away and whose wife had just happened to listen in on the party telephone line, came driving up full tilt even ahead of Francis, offering such comfort and support as a neighbour could until Francis could get there. When Francis came Harry helped him to get my father jacknifed into the back of the old Buick and they had driven him to hospital in Mafeking. He died there a week later, having never come out of his coma.

I could never hear without some measure of anguish the tale of his struggle to get that door open. As if the years had not already inflicted enough humiliation, his last conscious act must be useless, imbecile, leading only to frustration and petty irritation. Not enough is said for the quiet rational suicide. I don't suppose that my father would have resorted to suicide even if it were not still surrounded by such a mess of taboos—he had not the touch of melancholy to spark such an act. But towards the end the funerals of men who had been his neighbours and contemporaries made him broody and impatient, almost as if he thought Ed Brown or Ed Varma had pinched his death from him that he'd worked hard for, and earned, and left him hanging about naked and useless and tired and bored. . . .

If my mother was touched by the spectacle of this loyal and honourable man, her husband, sunk into senility, she gave no sign. She never allowed that he was other than wilfully cantankerous. It is quite probable that this attitude was what enabled her to survive her ordeal and cope with him. Indignation, which tends to devour me and leave me limp and ineffectual, has always seemed to put starch in her spine, fire in her eye and pounds of punch behind her left uppercut. She may well have needed all the indignation she could lay hands on over the years when she had, almost single-handed and by no means robust herself, to cope with my father's senility.

Whenever she got to that point in her recital at which Harry Brown and Francis came rushing to her in her hour of need, when her voice broke with the pity of *her* situation (that still-breathing remnant of humanity sprawled grotesquely across the

148

bed seemed relegated to the status of a theatrical prop dressing up her big scene), I just wanted to go away quietly and get lost.

But out into the hot Iowa night from Willie Loman's hotel I did not go, and eventually she changed the subject. She stopped the fragments of total recall and addressed me. She signalled an imminent expedition, of which I had no previous inkling. Before we turned up for lunch with Aunt Flora again tomorrow, as planned, we were to go to an address on East Euclid Street where we were to visit an old school friend of hers, one Dimple Schmunke. One would have thought that in Euclid there would have been no East nor West, in him no North nor South, but my mind would not stop to boggle upon that, it being urgently required for boggling upon the remarkable and unlikely chance which was upon me of meeting one Dimple (or Dymple) who must be, my mother calculated, now in her eightieth year.

As if that were not enough to stir the imagination, my mother mentioned that Dimple had had one sister, yclept Pink (or Pynk). Dimple and Pink! My mind did not have to reach out for an image of their dear mamma. She came, unbidden, of her own volition. Chiffon. Definitely chiffon and voiles, white parasols and a tinkling soprano voice given to *ingénue* renditions of 'The Blue-bird of Happiness'. Dimple and Pink she would name her delectable babies, and then tinkle off, leaving them to moulder away as ancient widows, still named Dimple and Pink. It was small wonder that Pink had had the foresight to die many long years before.

What, I wondered, should one say to eighty-year-old Dimple on the occasion of a first meeting? Impossible to prepare an opening. I would have to wait and play it by ear.

'Well, Dimple [or Dymple],' I could anticipate my mother saying. 'And what do you think of My Baby?' I'd just have to take it from there.

The next morning dawned brilliant and blistering. Against the possibility that Dimple and I would find that a little of each other went a long way, I sent my mother off to East Euclid Street by taxi bright and early, promising to find my way along in plenty of time to make, to the best of my ability, the requisite favourable impression on her friend before we should have to leave to keep our appointment with Aunt Flora. In any event I had some shopping to do, the toothpaste in my tube being nearly exhausted.

I strolled luxuriously about the hot streets, like some unrecognized fugitive from a zoo, wandering from shady spot to shady spot, found a cool soda-fountain and had a long cool drink, and generally enjoyed renewing contact with my own generation even if it simply meant communing with myself. And eventually, refreshed and fortified, I dispatched myself to East Euclid.

What I was not prepared for was to meet at the door the unmistakable remains of a breathtakingly beautiful woman. In fact I should hazard a guess that Dimple Schmunke is the most beautiful woman I have even seen, although she was no longer that beautiful by the time I met her. But still quite unmistakably something! Where other old women are almost invariably merely little old women, Dimple was *petite*. Her great dark eyes looked out of a face which struck you as delicate, even as you noticed its puffy unsunned pallor. She did not look old as my mother looked old. My mother might have been modelling for a classical Chinese painter studying the essence of ancient matriarchs who have survived the need for beauty or physical movement, whose eyes follow the brouhaha of children and grandchildren, who are content with occasional benevolent small tyrannies, with warmth and the prospect of a decent funeral at the end. In contrast, Dimple's childless body was still intact, as if it had been embalmed *vivant*; trim, delicate, faintly revolting.

She had been prepared for the arrival of 'the Baby', all right. As if I should be skipping up in my pink organdie party dress she had saved my treat—the pinkest ice-cream I have ever clapped eyeballs on, with chocolate-coated marshmallows on the side. Her tiny dim bungalow, hermetically resealed the moment I had been admitted, apparently boasted no refrigerator, for the ice-cream was soupy and the chocolate was grease-paint upon the sticky marshmallow. She fixed me with her enormous hunted-gazelle eyes, and was obviously going to be sick with disappointment if I did not enjoy my party, so I bolted the whole damned disgusting lot as quickly as my gorge would lie down, bidding a sad farewell to the enjoyment I had thought to find in one of Aunt Flora's delicious salad lunches. (Cold chicken, I thought. Refrigerator-chilled chicken chopped with apples and walnuts and a good brisk dressing.)

Dimple did all the talking. Her talk ran on and on as though she were hopped up on drugs or running a high temperature. She immediately picked up again the speech which she must have already been making at my mother for more than two hours. She said how alone she was in the world, how happy she was going to be when her blessed release came and she would find all her own folks again. She meant to find them again, to get her hooks into them again for all eternity. She appeared to believe— really believe—in the life eternal, but like so many who so do seemed to find this less a stimulus to serenity and patience in this vale of tears than cause for irritability. She mourned Papa and Mamma and Pink volubly, but not without noticing how inconsiderate they had been in abandoning her in this world. The late lamented Mr Schmunke was apparently not scheduled for admission to the family reunion, for he was never mentioned.

Strange to think that before that beauty had been ravaged by age there must have been armies of eligible young men milling about her doorstep, thrilling to her every vapid word, filling her every day—and her Mamma's ambitions for her daughter—with triumph. And now nothing was left to bear witness to the romantic love-play except perhaps this shabby, shuttered little frame bungalow. If her present worldly state was any criterion, she must have married Mr Schmunke for love, for there was no sign of money.

She disappeared into a bedroom and came out with old photographs of herself and Pink. Beautiful, beautiful gormless girls whose sole art appeared to have been blackmail extorted by helplessness, frailty, beauty and gormlessness. Like the names Dimple and Pink, the feminine blackmail technique would have been briefly and brilliantly appropriate, only to slide into irrelevance and then downright liability. I did not think much of the late Mr Schmunke. Even if Dimple had not married until she was getting on in years he would still have been a cradle-snatcher, so entrapped was she in her infant chrysalis. Still, his life with her could have been no picnic.

My mother, turning over the photographs, mentioned that she still had one from the time when she and Dimple had been roommates at the Teachers' College in Des Moines. Dimple knew instantly, without waiting for my mother to describe the photograph at all, which one it would be. She had never liked that one, she said. She had never felt that she looked well in that particular dress, and she should never have worn it for a photograph. She talked about her photographs as though they had some separate identity, like people whom she knew. It seemed quite probable that the photographs she had brought out for our delectation were literally enshrined in her bedroom, with candles and floral offerings and all.

Suddenly she turned to my mother, who sat through all her flap and flutter with cheerful imperturbability, and started consoling her, offering her pity, because my poor mother had had to endure such terrible experiences as being helpless to prevent her children from actually marrying and going off. She thought that it must be almost unbearable to be deserted by your own children! She stopped talking, obviously requiring some statement from my mother, who said mildly, 'Well . . .'

She turned to me then, and started burbling over what joy it must be to me to be able to travel like this with my dear Mamma, and how I would remember every moment of this experience, and treasure it all my life. She sent the authentic *frisson* down my spine, the one which stems from some implacable demonstration that free will is, for some persons at least, a delusion. Everything about her bespoke petrifaction long before the age of reflection and choice. Five years old. She had had to go all through life, through eighty intolerable years of it, being five years old. One might have been born to such a person, had one for a mother—*she* probably had, after all. One takes incalculable risks being born.

She did not step outside the door to make her farewells, but kept herself carefully inside, sheltered from the vast cloudless sky and dazzling sunshine, if not from the heat. She had closed her door carefully, and indubitably locked it, before we drove off.

My mother asked me what I had thought of Dimple.

'She must have been a very beautiful girl,' I said.

'Oh yes, Dimple was always pretty. Always very pretty,' said my mother.

She said it as if she had enjoyed Dimple's prettiness rather than having felt eclipsed by it—and if she were still enjoying it.

152

Suddenly I wondered if she had even seen the disturbing, embalmed creature I had just been watching, or if the Dimple of sixty years ago, the gazelle-eyed college girl, was not inscribed so indelibly on her memory that nothing short of death itself could alter the outlines. Perhaps indeed Uncle Frank was, until her own death should blot his out, her favourite young brother, the companion in adventure and mischief of seventy years ago. Perhaps she could barely make the connection between that boy and the skeleton threshing about on that hospital bed, so that the skeleton seemed hardly relevant. . . .

We did not see Dimple Schmunke again. But it was only a matter of days really—two or three weeks at most, and I believe Aunt Flora's letter containing the particulars was waiting for my mother when she got back to Canada—before the uneventful night of the quiet residential neighbourhood of East Euclid Street was filled with the screams of Dimple Schmunke. She screamed and screamed and screamed and would not open the door or speak to anyone. Finally the police had to break in, sedatives were brought in and administered, and the ambulance came and drove her off.

Although no screams had actually reached my ears, I was glad to get back to something as wholesome as Uncle Frank's dying after Dimple's living.

After the delicious lunch—I had to apologize to Aunt Flora for scarcely being able to touch it—I went up to see Uncle Frank again. I was prepared for him this time, and just sat down beside him without counting on communication. It was just as well, for he did not know me at all. He took my hand again, and stared and stared, but he couldn't get through. He asked me who I was, and I told him, but that was no help. He seemed rather distressed, as though he felt his failure might be interpreted as discourtesy, so I tried chatting. I told him that my mother and I were going first to visit Mortitia, the little town where they had spent their childhood, and that then we would be going on to visit Aunt June, who was their youngest sister.

He smiled immediately, and started to ramble on about Aunt June with brief but devastating accuracy.

'June? Never saw a woman who needed a good hairdo so badly. Don't suppose she'd even know what that means. . . .

153

Hard life. Work, work, work. All those cows . . . Joe never—
well, Joe never abusive. June so anxious to marry. Never Joe's
idea, that marriage. Not our business. . . .'

He rambled off then, sometimes into utter incoherence,
sometimes talking of persons and events unfamiliar to me, but I
sat quietly, forgotten, beside him for some time. He was utterly
vulnerable, utterly unable to secure any corner of his mind from
discovery. The unconscious had taken over and spread itself out
under the scrutiny of anyone who cared to come and see. But
nothing unseemly came forth. Sometimes his uncensored thoughts
were banal, sometimes humorous, sometimes muddled. There
were flashes of affection, of respect and magnanimity. It was
quite in character that the few words he should have spoken to
me while conscious of my identity should have been words of
comfort and encouragement. There seemed plenty of trivia, but
nothing obscene, or mean, or greedy. I began to see why, for all
her concern and her obvious affection for her husband, Aunt
Flora seemed so calm and undistressed. Even the rubbish of his
mind revealed a good man fulfilled. That she would miss him—
that she missed him now, for he was already gone from the
world of the living—was obvious. But his life had been a cause
for rejoicing, and she was too conscious of this to mess up its
end with her sorrowing.

I left him, feeling oddly comforted.

OVER THE LAST lap of our pilgrimage towards Mortitia,
that 'down home' which had never been displaced
from her heart, my mother's excitement rose to near
fever pitch and spilled over in the shape of statistics. 'Mortitia',
she said, 'is one thousand and twenty-three miles from Denver,
Colorado—or used to be.'

I was grateful for that 'used to be', as it was a lean time indeed for my sense of humour.

For although long-distance travel in America is plausible and even sometimes pleasurable, the short local journey provides a simple, inexpensive and salutary course on the retribution due to those who have neglected the customary offerings to the goddess of personal transport. Here, in the empire of the car which is meant to be lived in, absence of car is a sort of homelessness. One travels as exposed to discomfort and absurdity as a tortoise without a shell. Nothing is organized to cope with such a phenomenon.

To journey only a few miles we had to take a bus which dumped us nearly a mile from the railway station in a near-taxiless town. When we finally did manage to get to the station we waited four interminable hours in a stifling waiting-room whose wooden benches harboured invisible beds of nails. From this vantage point we could contemplate, like refugees without visas, those whose citizenship was properly established and documented, hurtling purposefully by on vast shining express trains which whistled contemptuously at us as they passed us by.

It is one thing to await the sound of the first cuckoo in spring with a wise passivity. It is quite another to await the condescension of a train in maximum discomfort. It roused in me a sort of fierce, sullen misanthropy.

Had I been alone I should hardly have noticed all this. I would have walked from the bus to the station without the worry about the taxi. I should have strolled about town while waiting, found a coolish and comfortable spot somewhere or something of interest to contemplate. But I didn't like to go off and leave my mother who, although happy enough, looked very weary indeed long before noon. Thus it was doubly aggravating to learn that inevitably the lunch counter we should have to patronize, and which was only a few yards from us on the other side of the railway lines, could only be reached by walking a long way down the line, crossing over and doubling back again.

I started loathing the station staff who provided a background to our discomfort, and the other discouraged, apathetic, sweating serfs in the waiting-room. At the lunch counter I was equally revolted by the grating voices loudly proclaiming sentiments of no content and the exhibition of teeth, fillings and all, that flashed in over-hearty laughter; by the spectacle of unneeded calories being shovelled in and the thorough and public picking of teeth afterward. Some of the men had scraggy necks, some pork-butcher necks, but all the necks were red. The women seemed to tan all right, but the men all looked sort of inflamed. The women seemed all thick bottoms and thin lips, with a Daughters-of-the-Revolution certainty in their faces. After lunch, when we got back to the station, I watched a man through the window facing away from the railway lines who was training a beautiful palomino horse to do show tricks. He wasn't ill-treating the horse or anything—indeed, I thought him both patient and skilful—but to reduce this beautiful creature to the performance of unnatural, gratuitous feats for squalid gain seemed the ultimate demonstration of the victory of the Yahoo.

My mother felt nothing of this. She enjoyed the passing trains, and followed each one in sentimental journey down the line to Mortitia. We were now, she said happily, twenty-seven miles from Mortitia by train, but thirty-four miles by road. Time was when all the trains on this line would have stopped at both stations, she said.

When we did finally arrive in Mortitia The Girls dominated the landscape. The first of The Girls were the Watts—so called because that had been their name fifty or sixty years ago before they had married. Two Watt Girls met us at the station—Bertha and Jessie. Bertha was driving. We were being domiciled with Jessie.

After supper that evening I excused myself and went outside to sit on the porch where I could make a few notes in peace, and feel private (for all that the porch was open to public view), and take stock of that street.

Mortitia, my mother had confided earlier in anticipation, had a population of 2,011. In her day it had stood at 2,008, or at least that was what they had said after the last census. The portion of the town sheltering those 2,011 souls which was visible from Jessie's front porch was, somewhat to my surprise, charming: modest little white frame houses set on unfenced lawns under truly magnificent elms and maples. There was a gentle sawing of cicadas—not a chorus, but something like an octet, I should think. As the darkness fell I saw for the first time in my life a

156

firefly, then another and another. They seemed infinitely touching in their tiny brevity, and I watched them spellbound until, as the evening turned to night and wore on a little, they seemed to have exhausted themselves and became more and more infrequent.

Inside I could hear my mother talking to Jessie. Jessie was the widow of a clergyman, the veritable ultimate in genteel respectability, and my mother's satisfaction at keeping such company was so off-putting that I made a note in my little journal to the effect that, Holman Hunt reproductions on all the walls or no Holman Hunt reproductions on all the walls, I must not automatically dislike Jessie.

Listening to their talk, I did not dislike Jessie. In fact I found myself warming to her. My mother was collecting facts and statistics as though they might be required as her price of admission at the Pearly Gates themselves. She and Jessie had a large common acquaintance—or had had—and she was gathering not only dates of deaths but times of day, witnesses, cause of death, next of kin and second next of kin. She told Jessie that she had no difficulty in remembering the date of her (Jessie's) husband's passing over because that also happened to be the birthday of her eldest grandson.

The first set of facts having been gathered and filed away, my mother started recollecting her journey to Mortitia, step by slow step. It was clear that Jessie was not going to be spared one minute detail. She would know the times of all arrivals and departures at all the major stations, the appointments of those stations we had passed through, the part of the journey where the train had lost a few minutes' time and where it had made it up again, what we had found to eat and when and where. Et cetera. Jessie, although not interested in this daunting dossier, sensed the pleasure my mother was extracting from this reconstruction, and she mustered what I took to be a sort of absentminded but kindly attention, encouraging my mother to continue her recitative whenever she showed signs of flagging, but without in all likelihood actually hearing much of it herself.

By the time I went to bed my misanthropy was burnt out, and I was thinking how you would mourn for fireflies if you had grown up with them as familiars. But I couldn't remember my mother or father ever even mentioning them.

Although we spent several days in Mortitia I was as it were only intermittently exposed to the town itself, my foreground being nearly always completely dominated by Girls. Early on I got an impression that this might perhaps be the first mortuary town (as one says dormitory town, or overspill town) that I had ever visited: except for a handful of business people needed to run the bank, the half-dozen shops and services, everyone seemed remarkably elderly. I inquired of Jessie, who said that in fact the population was largely made up of retired farmers from the neighbourhood, and their wives or widows. This probably accounted for the fact that the houses seemed to have escaped any tendency to outsize, overstuffing or straining after tomorrow. They seemed to be almost entirely neatly kept, nicely painted bungalows. And there were an astonishing number of substantial and prosperous-looking Protestant churches: Methodist, Adventist, Baptist.

One evening, when the heat of the day was losing its fiercer intensity and the shadows were growing longer and more efficiently enveloping, I walked all round the town. The sidewalks were grass-grown and crumbling where they were not completely absent, once you got away from the main commercial square and its approaches. The town might have been ghost, for all its sidewalks and pedestrians; I must have been almost pioneering some of them. For, although no one was more than twenty minutes' easy saunter from the heart of town, nobody walked. Even the elderly retired people who no longer drove themselves about seemed equipped with dependable relatives who chauffeured them to church, shopping or visiting. I found my walk curiously unnerving. Every small dog in town—there seemed to be nearly 2,011 of *them*—barked at me, spotting instantly a foreigner engaged in an inexplicable and un-American activity. Curtains twitched almost imperceptibly at windows, as though every house might hide one of those sly carnivorous *concierges* who conscientiously collect the raw material for blackmail or malicious mischief against half of Paris. I became aware finally of that curious little prickle of the spine dead between the shoulder-blades which has become over the years my personal Distant Early Warning System alert. Although I thought, looking around the dozing, tranquil, superannuated little town,

158

that my alert was a rather extravagant reaction, yet it had after all first manifested itself when I had been peacefully pursuing my solitary but lawful occasions afoot in God's Country.

I had spent a few weeks years before with my husband, who was training in the army camp at Fort Lewis in Washington state. I stayed in an off-camp hotel which was exclusive to officers and their families, I had no natural talent at all for the indolent, near-harem existence of the hotel, nor for hanging about the bar or reading magazines or playing bridge, and so I quickly fell into a routine of taking long walks through the wilderness of Douglas fir and bracken which stretched unbroken from our side of the army camp to the Pacific. I fondly hoped to penetrate the forest and discover the Pacific Ocean all by myself one day, but it was farther than it looked on the map, more fraught with obstacles; and most curiously all the little footpaths, which none but myself ever seemed to use, petered out in swamps or impenetrable tangles of shrubs. One morning, having washed my hair and rolled it up in curlers, I slipped out the back entrance of the hotel to dry it, walking in the spring sunshine, and had gone perhaps a mile from the hotel when I was suddenly startled by a sound behind me and turned to see a negro American soldier, who had apparently been lying in wait and ambushed me. He stood looking at me, casually dangling a commando knife which swung back and forth like a pendulum, held by its point. I looked back at him, and nobody said anything for what seemed quite some time. Finally, he asked where I was going. 'Nowhere,' I replied. 'Just out for a walk.' The improbability of *that* tale struck me immediately. If I had told him I was running to catch a bus it would have been no more absurd. He could have been alive a very long time, and hung around Douglas fir forests all day every day, without ever meeting a young blonde woman out for a walk! However, his attitude was not unreasonable; he was open to proof, so I made an extremely short speech, in as English an accent as I could muster and in a precise and formal language which he might recognize, I thought, as definitely foreign. I told him that my husband was a Canadian officer, that we were staying in the hotel (which I tried to sum-mon nearer, just beyond the farthest visible tree), and that walking was quite a common custom where I came from—which was not strictly true. He didn't say much, just enough to let me know that he was looking for a prostitute, and that he didn't intend to put up with any racial prejudice among the sisters of that sorority. Then we stood for a spell again while he mulled. I fancy that it was neither my foreign accent nor my (creditable) poise that finally did the trick, however, but the curlers in my hair. A working prostitute just does not go out with her hair rolled up in aluminium curlers and in flat walking shoes. He examined both head and feet carefully. Finally, he stood aside with a shrug, and let me pass, which I managed to do without unseemly haste and my knees actually did not turn to water until I was safely back among the harem. But as I walked away I felt that tickle, that little bull's-eye prickle on the spine dead between the shoulder-blades. . . .

(It is curious to tell this tale to armchair liberals. They assume immediately, even before the i's are dotted and the t's crossed, that the narrator hasn't understood the significance of the racialist thing behind all this, so they launch into the ABC of the pathology of racialism. Having slogged their way through that they seem affronted that anyone should object to being menaced in a wilderness—or anywhere else—by knives. If you can explain it, it's okay, they seem to feel, as they sit with *their* backs hugging the overstuffed armchair. Unrepentant, I refuse to like knives dangling at me regardless of the race, creed or colour of the hand that holds them. You never know when you're going to forget to put curlers in your hair before going out, after all, and then what?)

Mortitia, however, unsheathed no knives for me, despite the consternation as I politely requested an ash-tray wherever our little caravan came to temporary rest about town. I finally decided that the cigarette must have had some phallic symbolism for them, or some damn thing, for their reaction was often out of all proportion to any concern they could have felt for my health or welfare, or the odour clinging to their living-rooms or what-not. Bertha, the Watt Girl, was the first to decree flatly that she did not allow smoking in her house, so I went outside on to the porch swing and felt like an absolute devil, puffing away. Bertha's husband Harold, who owned the local garage and filling

160

station, surprised me by uttering some political reflections which would hardly have been common currency, I thought, among the local news sources and commentary. What for instance would happen if the United States actually *did* stop the arms race and the production of vast quantities of weapons and equipment? What would the steel industry do then, poor thing? He calculated, in his flat unemphatic drawl, that the unions would fight disarmament as frantically as big business itself if the chips were down. Nobody wanted a depression. They'd rather chance being able to ride the tiger interminably. I got the impression that Harold didn't much idealize the Little Man, or the Common Man, or even the American Way of Life. Not given to enthusiasms.

During the course of conversations between my mother and Jessie it was revealed to me that the man whom I shall always think of as my mother's 'suitor' was named August, and that he lived in Pea Ridge, Arkansas, of latter years. Although my mother mentioned that she had received a postcard from him depicting ostriches from the local zoo she unleashed no Dionysian laughter before the clergyman's widow, and did not break out the Third Dress.

One afternoon, when the Watt Girls were required to attend a meeting of the Women's Missionary Society, my mother and I were deposited with a Girl named Flora. The name was apt; her bathroom was a veritable jungle of tropical plants. Indeed it is only the second or third interesting bathroom I have ever encountered. The only other thing in her otherwise banal house which caught my eye was a plate which was hanging decoratively on the wall of the living-room. From across the room its bold black and red design demanded comment, so I inquired if she had been to Greece. She said that she hadn't, but that it was authentic Greek all right, a replica of a celebrated museum piece. She took it down and gave it to me to examine. In hand it turned out to be cheap and nasty and obviously mass-produced. She explained with great satisfaction that she belonged to the Buy Around the World Club, which will provide souvenirs—that was the word: souvenirs—from anywhere with no mess, no fuss, no travelling.

Jessie, who was well stocked with built-in kindness, could see that the excitement and travel were tiring my mother considerably, although she never mentioned it, and arranged more often than not that my mother's old friends and acquaintances should come to her, rather than that she should go to them. It meant a steady stream of persons in and out of the house, and endless sandwiches and pastries and cups of tea and coffee. My mother, having lived most of her life in a farm where food is the only commodity in abundance without much cash outlay, did not notice that all this entertaining might be doing violence to Jessie's visibly slender income, especially when added to the cost of feeding the two of us over several days. I insisted on doing all the shopping for the entertaining myself, and used to bring home bits and pieces of extras for ourselves so that she should not be too much out of pocket. I am sure it was no lack of generosity in her that made her acquiesce in this arrangement. What I found more of a strain than parting with oddments of cash, however, was the effort I felt compelled to make organizing, serving and washing up after all these things, and being 'My Baby', but it didn't seem fair to saddle Jessie—no longer young and spry herself—with all of that, so I soldiered on pretty manfully.

The evidence I had of my mother's fidelity to Mortitia and all who sailed in her continually astonished me, even though I had been vaguely aware of it all my life. She had subscribed to the *Mortitia Mercury* all during the years of exile, of course, and had studied that thrilling weekly as if it were a love letter. Not only had she read the contents, she remembered them. She could tell the natives what was happening at the other end of their own street although they might be ignorant of it themselves. She could give news of the long-absent mutual acquaintance because she remembered that two-sentence filler inserted at the end of column three, page five, away back in October 1949 (and she would very likely remember that the paper from which she had learned it *was* from October 1949 too). She knew which buildings had been razed since her departure, which had been built, the owner and what it was used for. She was curiously impartial, receiving or dispensing with equal interest or emphasis the news that old Mrs So-and-So has seven grandchildren and three great-grandchildren, or that Mr Thingummy died millimetre by millimetre of a particularly excruciating form of cancer or

162

that the W.M.S. now holds its monthly meetings in the Odd-fellows' Hall.

And in and out of Jessie's little house, with its Holman Hunt reproductions, moved platoon after platoon of Girls. If any of my mother's male contemporaries, other than old Julius, were still extant, they were keeping very quiet about it, although she may have seen some of them the day Bertha took her to visit the Star of Evening Home for Senior Citizens suffering from assorted incapacities. She came back in a state of exhausted bliss that day, announcing that they had had a 'regular orgy', which she pronounced with a hard 'g' that seemed somehow appropriate to the occasion.

It was with great satisfaction that she noted that her score of grandchildren and great-grandchildren was second to none, and well ahead of most.

Most of the Girls, on being presented with 'My Baby', gave me a figurative pat on the head and forgot about my existence, which seemed the best thing to do until the sandwiches were passed. Two or three were openly (if briefly) censorious when it transpired that I lived in Britain. They might well have echoed Queen Victoria's 'abroad is bloody' had they known about it but not who had said it. When a brace of octogenarians actually displayed some interest in England, and uttered some commendatory words about English politics, civilization and the arts, my mother cut that thread of conversation with scant ceremony, partly because her youthful Anglophobia was again in full spate, now that she was back at the source, and partly because she had no intention of wasting precious time on general conversation. It had been all very well, my talking with Aunt Flora or Dr Baron even. But we were here, in Mortitia, à la recherche du temps perdu, and that was too serious a business to be cluttered up with anything of such recent vintage as me.

In fact, the morning I spent mowing Jessie's vast lawn with a great heavy mower that had never been intended for the use of a seven and a half stone woman (I ached from the neck down for about four days, and worked up an impressive set of blisters) seemed one of my less arduous, more relaxed mornings.

Jessie and Arthur (her late departed) had at one time spent ten years as missionaries to the Osage Indians on a Reserve in

Oklahoma. I inquired after their traditions and customs. Having never known any Indians personally, nor sampled the environment of any Reserve, I wondered what might have remained to them from their ancient paraphernalia which would still serve them in the twentieth century on the Reserve, but all I could get from Jessie was a catalogue of their failures to measure up to her norms; they 'didn't like to work' (I could have guessed that, for none of the North American Indians, so far as I know, have succumbed to workomania); they were not sensible about money; no matter how hard one worked to educate them, they sloughed off their learning and reverted to their old ways the moment they were out of school. Her very considerable capacity for empathy could not apparently transcend that sort of barrier, and I was pleased not to have known her missionary self which, after the fashion of missionary selves, was certain that it represented a standard from which departure could only mean inferiority. If any Indian had had any separate identity for her, no memory of it seemed to remain now. She spoke of them with patience, with boredom, with irritation, but without a trace of affection.

One day a man turned up at the door asking to see my mother. His name was Newell Finegal, and his joy at their reunion was almost tearful. She was pleased to see him too. He explained to me that he had been in my mother's class at school when he was ten years old, and that he could remember it all like yesterday. Indeed they recalled pranks and snippets of reminiscences in extraordinary detail, items so small and of such little import that one would have thought that they would have been irrevocably silted up years ago by the debris left by even the most humdrum life, but apparently one would have been wrong. As my mother had not taught for fifty years I realized, with something like revulsion, that Newell, for all that he looked a soft, drab, moisty forty-fiveish, must in fact have been not less than sixty years old.

As if it were an ardently polished apple, he offered my mother the information that she was the finest teacher he had ever had, probably the best that Mortitia had ever had. She accepted this with serene pleasure, as her due—and indeed it may well have been accurate. He said that school had certainly never been the same for him after my mother left. He reminded her that his mother had died just about the time when she had become his teacher. He did all but climb into her ancient lap to be comforted.

Of course he ran Mortitia's solitary laundry and dry cleaning establishment now, since his father's retirement. He told my mother in the greatest confidence (like the Girls, he was utterly untroubled by my existence, and probably scarcely aware of it) that he had been engaged for fourteen years to a lady named Ruby who lived some miles away in the next town down the line. He managed to convey this information so that it left no room for doubt that this engagement involved a little poaching on the old marital privileges. Then he awaited with anxiety some sort of absolution. My mother continued to beam at him, even as she must have done fifty years before when he came bursting in to show her his lunch-pail full of tadpoles. He cheered up considerably.

It was with some surprise that I learned then that Newell was in fact the only son of one of my father's rare surviving cousins, Julius Finegal, of whom my father had often spoken with great affection; they had been boys and young men together. Newell had come, it turned out, with the intention of inviting us to visit his father after supper.

Julius was eighty-nine, a big hearty man with a cheerful leathery face and one leg amputated. Except for his ready generous chuckle he bore no resemblance that I could see to my father. His memory was one mad scramble. He did seem to remember who we were, but if he asked my mother once he asked her a score of times—during the three or four hours we sat there on their porch watching the sunset fade into darkness and then the darkness fill with the tiny fountains of fireflies puffing up from the cornfield across the road—how Ed (my father) was, and why he hadn't come with us. My mother explained firmly but courteously each time that Ed had been dead for four years already. Oddly enough she became irritable because he kept telling us that he was ninety-three instead of eighty-nine, and she corrected him with ever-increasing severity. You'd have thought that the four years he was adding to his age were some unmerited promotion. I tried to reconcile her to his conviction, suggesting that if *he* hadn't a right to be wrong about his own age, who had? He laughed and laughed, but my mother was just as annoyed as ever when, fifteen minutes or so later, he told us that he was ninety-three.

Newell prowled about like a leopard, caged by his own inadequacies and his father's infirmities. When he had a chance he told my mother, out of the old man's hearing, that Ruby wouldn't take on the old man—and who could blame her? He looked close to tears. The old man wet himself, without apparently noticing it, while we sat there.

My mother interrogated Newell about August, the suitor, of Pea Ridge, Arkansas, at some length. She seemed anxious to establish his condition now and position in life, but Newell had only very small change in his pocket on that subject. Afterwards my mother said to me, almost as if I were one of her Girls instead of My Baby, that she hadn't dared to reveal 'all', for although Newell might have understood the old man might well have been indiscreet!

A day or so later, when I was downtown shopping for the daily Danish pastries and chocolate éclairs for the next wave of teas, I passed the laundry, and Newell, who was serving behind the counter, rushed out with an invitation to join him for coffee. He rounded up someone from the back to take over and we went out to the coffee-shop. He apologized a little anxiously because he couldn't buy me a drink, but as Mortitia certainly, and the whole state of Iowa if I am not mistaken, was bone 'dry' it was manifestly impossible. I assured him that I could live without alcohol, but asked whether he did not sometimes find it oppressive. But members of the American Legion could get beer in the American Legion Club, he cried thankfully, and he was a member. I probed a little, looking for some spark of revolt against the Women's Christian Temperance Union who were governing his life in this matter (especially as, to my thinking, one's gratitude for the privilege of drinking American beer might be deservedly diluted), but I was fishing around in the wrong man. He did not mind, even appeared to *like* the W.C.T.U. around to impose their authority. But his trouble was with the scarcity rather than the excess of female dominion.

Eventually of course Sunday rolled around and we rolled off to church, Jessie's Christian Adventists' Church. Bertha and

Harold called for us in the car. My curiosity had been mildly whetted already by a green cardboard bookmark which was in service in the only book I ever saw in Jessie's home—her Bible—which had its allotted place on the living-room coffee-table. On the bookmark was worked out an anagram of a religious message which simultaneously advertised Mr Holdcraft's *Snappy Sermon Starters*, which indispensable small handbook was available for a small fee from the Abingdon Press. It had been agreeable to weigh Mr Holdcraft against Holman Hunt for dominance in the living-room, and after such a start one could but feel that further religious ventures could scarcely lack some exotic features.

We sat in the front pew of the neat little church, as befitted the clergyman's widow and her *entourage*. The minister was a visiting celebrity and a near-perfect pink jelly version of John L. Lewis, the trades union giant. From under the celebrated beetling brows issued forth pink-jellied lightnings which were punctuated by a shaking of pink-jellied jowls. One might fancy that the plumpish body, unexposed to the vagaries of wind and weather, might have been a suitable blancmange to accompany just such a jelly. He got straight down to business as soon as it was sermon time.

There was no need (I gathered) for the brethren to falter or suffer doubts, nor to be embarrassed by the unseemly laughter of those who had not seen the light. The fact that none of the millenial prophecies made had yet borne fruit did not mean that the prophets had been wrong, nor that the millenium would not come, having been appropriately foretold. He then proceeded to recall a quite remarkable number of instances of millenniums foretold, of the faithful gathering on mountain tops or haystacks or seashores according to the inspiration (assemblies invariably ordained at awkward locations at excruciating hours) to await The End, only to have to trudge back home and try to get some breakfast out of the refuse they had left when nothing but the Last Trump had been anticipated. It seemed an odd way to buoy up faint hearts and sinking spirits, his cataloguing of prophetic failures and of the mirth they had provoked.

But then he weighed into the villains of the piece—the papists, first, as incorporators of paganism and polluters of the

Word. Who knew what tampering with texts had not been done while there had been none but Roman Catholics to keep custody of the sacred books? Then he severely censured Caesars Julius and Augustus who had, it seemed, loused up the calendar and even time itself, thus throwing the calculations of prognosticators according to the Book of Revelation all out of kilter. He seemed to harbour a dark suspicion that the aforementioned Caesars had perpetrated the aforementioned mischiefs deliberately and with malice aforethought, meaning to sow consternation among the ranks of the faithful. He next graciously approved of Luther, Calvin, Knox, Wesley and assorted other worthies who had done what they could to sort out the mess. He ended his dissertation with fulsome congratulations to the assembled congregation and their friends and associates, assuring them that they would be seated with the Prosecution on Judgment Day.

I found it increasingly difficult to believe that adult men and women who were presumably competent to manage their worldly affairs, people who came in out of the rain instead of just standing around outside complaining of the wet, could actually listen to this stuff. It didn't seem to embarrass Jessie or my mother at all. Visitor and guest or not, my curiosity was not to be stifled, and I turned round for the odd quick stare at the congregation. The little church was as full as a bingo hall. Not one face registered anything but respectable euphoria. Even Harold, who had had the wit to give some thought to the hold the arms race had got on the American Way of Life, was the picture of passive approval. Rows of plump glazed buns, peacefully baking in their hot little oven of a church. Or half baking.

After lunch Harold and Bertha called and took us all for a drive a few miles out into the country in search of Gus, a farming community where my mother's family had lived until she was fourteen, at which time the family had moved to the fringe of Mortitia itself. Later, as a teacher, she had for a little while lived and taught in that neighbourhood again.

I was thankful that the distance was not far, and that we were on very back-country roads which were nearly deserted, for although Harold was not a farmer he drove like one, inspecting crops, houses, livestock—anything and everything but the road itself. He pointed a lot, and sometimes had no hands on the steering-wheel. I was petrified. Bertha and Jessie were so accustomed to it that they apparently did not notice it. My mother was happy beyond belief. She named every farm, according to the name of its owner of sixty years ago, as magisterially as Adam naming the beasts. The farms, although not as lush and rich-looking as some we had seen, were well kept and pleasant and filled with hot July promise. The rolling country with its fine elms was good to look at, if only the car would stop heading first for one ditch then for the other, only to be recalled at the last minute with a jerk.

The same family still lived just across the road from the house of my mother's infancy, and we dropped in. The family was at home, and hospitable. There was a grandparent of my mother's generation, a son in his fifties with his wife and their adult invalid son, pinched and grey and suffering in his wheel chair; and another (visiting) married daughter and her husband, and two or three youngish children running about, who showed me the family wonder—a burnt-out meteorite about three inches in diameter, and unbelievably heavy, which had fallen near the house.

The remoteness of this house, and of the life which was lived in it, from all the stock Americas which are fabricated for export struck me forcibly. There was the shabby linoleum covering the floors, the worn, bony, uncompromising chairs, the *décor* which was a negation of the possibility of decoration, and yet on the whole not unhomely; a suspicion that Sunday dinner was still special with them, the food good, the good humour and unaccustomed leisure of the Sabbath still meaningful. The young children obviously enjoyed being visitors in that house, and you can't fool young children about the atmosphere of houses. The people too were worn and anonymous, but like my mother they were eroded rather than broken, people submitting to age or illness but not rejected and being scrapped as obsolete. The absence of the trappings of success didn't seem to worry anyone. Except for the invalid, who had stopped trying to conceal his fretfulness, they all seemed whole persons. Nobody tried to push the wheel-chair into any unobtrusive corners.

After leaving their house we descended upon what had once been the community centre, where the little white frame church and ditto school stood, both now empty. And the graveyard.

Harold drove us into the graveyard, and we got out of the car again.

Here were the graves of my mother's parents, and a scattering of aunts. She progressed regally, flanked by Watt Girls, from headstone to headstone, and they discussed the departed family and neighbours casually, affectionately, as though death (if it existed at all) had no sting. The Watt Girls' parents were here too, and their only brother had been buried here more than half a century before, having never regained consciousness after they brought him home with head injuries from the football field. They relived with serenity the old anguish of it, and how the boy's Papa had never got over it, never.

I wondered if my mother hankered after resting here. Since our arrival in Mortitia the people and the *manes* of this place had seemed to have so much more reality and significance for her than those of her exile—not excluding, I had thought at times, her own children and grandchildren. Now I tagged along attentive to their talk, but no note of regret, of deprivation, ruffled her communion with the dead. When she had finished she departed the little graveyard in peace. In her own good time, and fortified by her journey, she would return to us.

M Y AUNT JUNE, I am told, was with us when I was born. Whether she actually assisted the doctor in delivering me I couldn't say; she was still practising her profession of nursing at that time, and would have been considered competent to work with him; on the other hand the threshers were on the farm—some twelve extra ravenous men to be fed, their food to be the best the house could provide and served promptly—and it is possible that she was more urgently required in the kitchen than in my mother's bedroom.

And indeed after meeting Aunt June I was inclined to hope that she had been slaving over a hot stove and masses and masses of vegetables. I would rather the doctor had smacked the howl into my shocked and purpling nakedness, that I should have had a few hours to adjust to the world before being exposed to her— just in case there is something to the fairy-tales, to the qualities conferred by those ancient women who used to cluster at the cots of the helpless. Technically I suppose Aunt June wasn't all that old when I was born, but it is difficult to imagine that she was ever young either.

I didn't meet her again after the time of my birth until that same trip on which I had first encountered Uncle Frank, and there had seemed some doubt that all memory of her might have been eclipsed by the difficulty of locating her at all. My mother had of course furnished us with her address. We knew that she and Uncle Joe lived on a farm, and that their postal address was Rural Route Six, Runnerton, Indiana. The natives all spoke our lingo, and it had seemed but the work of a moment, once we had found our way into the little one-horse town, to get adequate directions.

'Aha!' we said, using our rational educated loaves in harmony, working towards a solution of our problem. 'Who will of necessity know the location of a farm on R.R. 6? Who indeed? The Post Office, that's who,' we said, and congratulated one another on arriving so soon at the obvious—nay, only sure— solution. And so, holding the bit of paper on which my mother had written the address in her strong and unequivocal hand- writing, I popped briefly into the post office.

'Could you please tell me how to get to this address?' I inquired politely of the man labelled Inquiries.

He took the piece of paper, studied it, turned it over, turned it back and studied it again. He disappeared into a back room and returned presently accompanied by another man.

'Where'd you get this?' inquired the other man, holding up my piece of paper.

'From my mother. Why?'

'Whatcha want with these people anyhow? What's this address to you?'

'Mrs Helge is my aunt—my mother's sister. I want to visit her.'

M

They exchanged knowing glances.

'What business you got with her then?'

'No business. Just a social call. Just driving through and stopping long enough to say hallo.'

'Nothin' to stop anybody from sayin' they're just drivin' through, is there?'

'From Canada,' I insisted.

'Nothin' to stop anybody from claimin' to be drivin' through from Canada.'

'Why would anyone bother?'

One of them leaned forward across the counter, real confidential like. 'That's what we'd like to know . . . .'

It was the back room of an Edward G. Robinson film. I was apparently emissary for sinister forces, or possibly I was the sinister force myself. Quite an achievement in blue jeans and a car-crumpled shirt. They'd have probably been sadly disappointed to learn that my blonde hair was natural; it took a bleach job, in them days, to qualify you as a moll.

At about this point my husband, tired of drumming on the steering-wheel to himself, came in.

'Got it?' he asked.

'Has she got what?' inquired one of the Robinsons, managing to look as though his mouth was toying with a large and expensive cigar, although in fact all he had was a pencil behind one ear.

'The directions,' said John.

'You seem awful all-fired anxious to get those directions,' said the man.

'They're playing third degree,' I said. 'We're a dastardly plot.'

'There,' said a Robinson. 'You admit it.'

I produced a nickel. 'Perhaps you would phone Mrs Helge and ask if she is expecting her niece and husband from Canada this week, and if it's all right to give them directions.'

'Oh,' said one of the wise guys. 'So this is your "husband" . . .'

John looked about ready to start creating. I took my nickel back. 'I'll phone Aunt June,' I said. 'She can give us the directions herself.'

The Robinsons' laconic gazes followed us laconically to the call-box. I studied the directory. No telephone. We left the post office and tried a couple of stores and the bank. Blank. I don't know whether we were too close to the Al Capone country—Chicago is more or less just around the corner—or whether people had just been seeing too many tough-guy pictures to resist the roles. Finally, we were obliged to go back and solicit the help of the Robinsons again if we were to find the farm at all. They took down lengthy descriptions of us, the make and licence number of the car (we could hardly have been thought ideally equipped to carry out any funny business as we were travelling in the only Hillman Minx between the Mason-Dixon Line and the Canadian border and were right smack in the middle of the Ford/General Motors territory: so inconspicuous were we that we had only to stop anywhere for five minutes to be smothered by gapes of small boys), and told us how to find the farm.

After all that Aunt June had come as something of an anti-climax, and I was only half appreciative of her unique, very female, Mad Hatter quality. She was an odd little person under her busy, busy hair. Although she had been forewarned, our arrival seemed to throw her into near panic. Joe wasn't there. That was the long and the short of it. We had come and Joe wasn't there. He was teaching. Did we know that Joe was a teacher? People didn't always appreciate Joe, she said, but he was teaching in the agricultural college. He really knew his farming, she said, and how to teach others. Joe had done a lot with his life. If she inquired into what sort of trip we were having, or asked after anyone left behind in Sunny Alberta, it was in a fit of absent-mindedness while the higher zones of the brain were thinking up ways of conveying the loss we were undergoing. She might have been the proprietor of some small provincial zoo whose only lion is dead or indisposed. And she was having a little trouble disciplining her new false teeth.

Finally she bethought herself, it being late mid morning, and made us some coffee. When we had finished that we seemed to have been equipped with the natural break, so we took it and left, Aunt June following us out to the car, still talking about Joe. She may have been a little vague as to who we were or why we had come, but she was certainly hoping that she had acquitted herself well.

I must say I was not expecting anything very spectacular in the way of entertainment in Indiana during this return engagement. Superimposed on my ten-year-old memory of Aunt June and her paragon was now Aunt Minnie's reaction to them. She saw them fairly frequently, and when she had spoken of June—'When I think of my baby sister!'—it had been to mist over completely, while Joe's name reduced her to speechless indignation. She accused Joe of working his wife like an animal. My mother, who had never been any great fan of Joe's either, was none the less inclined to argue. She figured that June *liked* to work like an animal. Joe let her, all right, but she wasn't sure that Joe *made* her do it.

'Well, I don't know,' Aunt Minnie would say. 'All I know is I just can't bear to see her go on the way she is. Joe shouldn't let her.'

It was even more arduous getting to Indiana this time. We caught a train from Mortitia to Chicago, where we had to change. The long, long walks from the platforms into the station waiting-rooms and back out to the platforms again might have tired the young and brisk in that heat. My mother was trembling with exhaustion long before we got to our coach, and there was no bench anywhere on the platform where she could sit and rest for a minute or two. Perhaps God was expected to help the old or infirm; certainly nobody else appeared to be giving them a thought. I offer Chicago Central Station—and any others of the ilk who might like one—a ready made motto, free: IF YOU CAN'T LOOK ALIVE, DROP DEAD!

Once on the train we had a brief and quite remarkably unlovely journey through mile after hideous mile of what appeared to be grain storage elevators, cement plants, factories, warehouses as blind and brutal as Gestapo interrogation centres. Finally, after a few miles of more rural scenery, we arrived at our sizzling destination, faced with yet another quarter-mile walk to the station along the cinder path beside the tracks. The Paragon himself met us, and we hoisted my mother somehow into the dizzy heights of the cab of his farm track, got ourselves in and set off. He was inclined to be hospitable, I decided, in his loud, red-faced way I had somehow been expecting something a little more surly. My mother had frequently related some of her heated debates with him in times past; they tended to disagree about grammar and pronunciation, and she took a school-marm's privilege of correcting him, to which he replied with a male's prerogative of knowing better than the female. I was rather surprised that they seemed to strike no sparks off each other. I put it down to mother's exhaustion, and the euphoria which had settled over her apparently for the duration of her trip. But Joe was certainly not trying to brew up quarrels, as I had vaguely thought he might.

My mother inquired after June.

'Well,' he said, 'you'll find that she ain't getting any younger.' Then he proceeded to point out that he too was not getting any younger, and that *his* back had been giving him trouble lately. . . .

Indeed Aunt June appeared to have aged about twenty years since I had seen her ten years previously. Although she was actually ten years younger than my mother, she looked more like five to ten years older. Above all she was senile. Her Hatter's Madness had progressed beyond the comic or the colourful to the pitiful. Her senility was not cheerful like old Julius, or serene like my father, but anxious, needling her into charging off in all directions, rendering her competent in none. To watch her coping with her simple everyday life was like watching someone performing a protracted self-mutilatiom.

She had only time to greet us briefly and vaguely before she took off to see to the milking and feed the pigs. The barns were fairly well equipped—she didn't have to milk her twelve or fifteen Holsteins by hand or anything like that—but nevertheless a young man would not have seemed out of place doing the work which this diminutive, exhausted-looking woman of seventy with those sickeningly bewildered eyes charged into morning and evening. And with Joe's 'bad back' he could hardly be expected to lift anything heavy, like pails of milk or pig feed, now could he? Aunt June was very worried about Joe's bad back, and spoke of it repeatedly. And after the milking there was all that washing up of equipment in the dairy. Although it seemed highly unlikely that anything was actually made clean, the ensuing fatigue would probably have been as great as if her labours brought the dairy up to operating theatre standards.

She emerged breathless but triumphant from barn and dairy

and plunged immediately into supper. Alas. For she was quite
unbelievably filthy. When we had first come in I had been impressed by her neglect of herself. The remembered magpie's
nest of hair, greyer than when I had last seen it, was scattering
hairpins with gay abandon. Finger-nails had been neither trimmed
nor cleaned since heaven only knew when. Useless to wonder
how often she bathed; it might have been last week or last year,
and the state of her memory was such that my guess would have
been as good as hers. But I doubt if even she was often quite as
fouled as she was on that first evening of our visit. During her
milking she had apparently, in some fit of absence of mind,
stationed herself in the direct line of fire behind a cow with
loose bowels and a bad cough, and her apron was plastered with
half-dried filth. Oblivious to this, she charged about her kitchen
rejecting all offers of assistance with some warmth, as though
they implied some lack of confidence in the management (they
did!). She did not even wash her hands. She could not remember
from one minute to the next what she was doing, where anything
was, what we might have to eat. She looked in the oven for the
things that were in the fridge. She took the lettuce and tomatoes
out of the fridge, then looked in it for them again five minutes
later and almost had a fit because she thought they hadn't been
sent with the grocery order. (She had a standing order for
groceries, having long since given up trying to figure out what
they actually needed. I once stumbled upon a vast hoard of
powder for scrubbing out sinks and bathtubs; she had apparently
not noticed that she might have reduced, or even cancelled, that
item for a few years. Fascinating to think what some archaeologist
in some far future day might conclude about our civilization if he
should unearth *that* treasure. . . .) When she looked into the
freezer compartment to see if anything there would remind her
of what was for supper she forgot to put the ice-cream back and
it melted all over the place long before supper. At one point she
vaguely flapped a lettuce in the general direction of the sink and
this, with a couple of unwashed tomatoes and some of that
revolting commercial salad cream, turned out to be salad. The
cold ham looked pretty good to me until she had fingered every
slice of it. There was, I thanked heaven, yogurt in a sealed
container. Yogurt I can take or leave as a rule, but on that

occasion I declared myself passionately addicted to yogurt. I announced that I could practically live off the stuff and would like nothing better than to be presented with it three times a day. But no hint was taken.

I ate the supper grimly, as a bacteriologist obliged by thirst and social custom might accept a glass of water raw from the Ganges. I thought of all the millions of foreigners who believe that America lives sterilized, wrapped in cellophane, and surrounded by a moat filled with disinfectant—and I wished they were right.

I entertained brief hopes that I might be allowed to wash the dishes after supper. Some of them were harbouring some pretty interesting archaeological data, layer upon layer. But Aunt June wouldn't have it. I was allowed to wipe, and for the duration of our stay—only a couple of days, for which I was thankful—that was as close as I got to meddling in her kitchen. On more than one occasion I had to slip out unobtrusively for a quiet little retch, but I was never actually sick. If my mother noticed anything amiss she met it with unshakable poise.

And it's an ill wind. My abstemiousness, coupled with a tendency toward leanness, gave Uncle Joe the occasion for many a merry quip. He thought I was dieting—afraid of getting fat. In fact for most of my life I have eaten industriously, just to keep from disappearing entirely. However, it seemed a good idea to let him have me dieting, so we chucked calorie counts back and forth. He, it seems, had a slight tendency towards high blood pressure, along with his bad back and a threatened duodenal ulcer. It was no wonder his wife had to look after him, even if he was ten years her junior—as he was—and young-looking for sixty, with plenty of good red meat on his substantial bones. Aunt June wasn't taken in by his superficial appearance of health. Not her. When I inquired for the ash-tray I was told in no uncertain terms that she would have no smoking in her house. It was not a morals charge this time though. Joe, it seemed, had a tendency towards asthma. I did my smoking outside.

It was as good a locale as one could have asked for to meditate upon the inscrutable ways of providence, if you are bent in that direction. Take Aunt Minnie now, weeping over her little sister's condition, vilifying Joe. One could see her point. Great strapping self-advertising loud oaf, overseeing the farm, doing all the light work or the lofty status-laden jobs, and leaving the burdens to his aged, near-dotty wife. It didn't look good. But it is not unlikely that if Aunt Minnie had suddenly become the management, and had reversed their roles, with June being cherished and coddled, June would have curled up and died of it. Being Joe's doormat, faithful dog and public relations agency was her vocation. Joe accepted it; I saw no evidence that he extorted it. Indeed the number of men who could have put up with it must be fairly limited (I hope it is!). There was no sign that he was mean about money. Quite a lot of it had been spent on the furnishings in the house. Not that they were interesting, except in so far as they proved that a true Mad Hatter can put her imprint on anything, even the most mass-produced Sears-Roebuck three-piece chesterfield suite. The kitchen equipment was more than adequate. It is not impossible in fact that theirs was an ideal marriage, if you happen to have that sort of idealism.

Indeed, so all-in-all to Aunt June was her Joe and his qualities and achievements that she appeared even to have abandoned her past. In vain my mother tried to rouse in her some memory of ancient, shared, family life. Aunt June just fogged up entirely. She could apparently remember almost nothing. She ventured once to say that she had lived as a child on a farm only thirty or forty miles from Mortitia, in Iowa. This should have been thirteen or fourteen miles. I expected my mother to spring immediately to the defence of Fact—I don't know that I have ever known her to pass up such an opportunity (or duty, as I suppose she considers it). But she said nothing. I believe that she was genuinely touched by Aunt June—was shocked into seeing her as she was rather than as she had been sixty years ago. She did not offer her any advice, and was unbelievably mild towards Joe, patiently listening to his celebration of his achievements, wisdom, the soundness of his opinions on any and every subject.

I was at this time tentatively classifying myself as a writer—people expect you to be something—but carefully qualifying the description by adding that I was not noticeably successful. So when Joe asked me what I did I told him that I was an unsuccessful writer. He ignored the qualification and came up with the absolute certainty that I wrote for the *Reader's Digest*. No, I explained, I'm trying to break into the television field at the moment. But a writer for the *Reader's Digest* he had made me, and a writer for the *Reader's Digest* I must be. What is more, he had a commission for me. He had always fancied himself as 'The Most Unforgettable Character I Have Met', which is his very favourite reading matter, and he set out deliberately to *be* the most unforgettable character *I* had met, so that I should immortalize him. There was a certain lack of decision on his part as to whether he should be unforgettable as a philosopher, as a success story or as a card. The success story, oddly enough, I found quite tolerable. For an illiterate youth, unable to speak English, who had come to America with nothing but the clothes he stood in, he had achieved a good deal: independence, enough knowledge that others came to him to get it, fifteen acres of near waste land cunningly converted into a little gem of balanced productivity, the pigs and the cows providing just the right amount of fertilizer for the corn and the orchard, the orchard and the alfalfa yielding not only fruit and cattle feed, but honey. I learned about nitrate deficiencies in corn. Unlike many a self-made man he seemed without greed. His fifteen acres and his little fame at the local agricultural college sufficed.

But he wouldn't stick to his success story. He *would* philosophize. The very cracker barrel groaned with the boredom of his philosophy. Yet even the philosopher was attractive in comparison with the card. Think of the most embarrassingly unfunny film comic who has ever made you squirm. Think of people to whom club feet, hunchbacks and hare-lips are knee-slappingly comic. Uncle Joe, the card, seemed to come at me from all directions. I'm not at all sure that he was not worthy of the *Reader's Digest*; certainly he was as importunate as their subscription department.

But in the end the most unforgettable thing about Uncle Joe was this: Uncle Joe was a Quaker, a member of the Society of Friends.

I have never been present at a meeting of the Society, but understand that it is customary for the members to sit in silent meditation until such time as the spirit shall move someone to speech. All I have to say is, I should just have liked an opportunity to watch Joe waiting, passing up golden opportunities to have the first and last word. I was curious enough about it to have asked him to take me to a meeting had we stayed over Sunday. But we didn't.

We left June and her Joe to their idyll, and they were possibly as glad to be left as I was to be gone. (Never have packaged sandwiches peddled on trains tasted so good to me as those with which I broke my near-fast as we left Indiana for Chicago and points west and north.) Everything seemed to be their own unique version of shipshape, and they were safe among their cows and pigs and bees and corn and apples, and Joe's hypochondria and brilliance and Aunt June's addled energies. One felt they would muddle through successfully to some respectable end.

One is not necessarily prophetic. During the plague of tornadoes which hit the Middle West during the spring of 1965 they were cleaned out—nothing left but their house. Aunt June was in it when the wind struck and so was uninjured. Joe was standing near a manure spreader in the barn when it was stove in, but the machine stopped the beams from crushing him and he got off with a slight shoulder injury. (It must have been very slight, for Joe was the person who so designated it.) He sold the cattle for about half price. When he wrote to my mother he was waiting for the bulldozer to come in and clear up the debris of fruit trees, buildings, etc., and he struck, naturally enough, an elegiac note: 'June is in a nursing home until we get established. I am in a friend's home. It could be that the future is dim.'

In a nursing home! Without her Joe to coddle and care for, what chance has Aunt June to keep her tenuous grasp of reality?

Or will the immigrant boy make good again, in his late sixties, so that June's surviving relations can polish up their clucks of disapproval as they behold her slaving away for him, cherishing his happy hypochondria, and Joe, plump and rosy, peaceably letting her get on with it . . .?

MY JOURNAL ended with June and Joe, and I almost forgot Uncle Ray entirely. It would have been a natural enough thing to do. Even my mother, who persists in all her relationships, whether they be good, bad or indifferent, has had some difficulty in remembering his existence, or at least she never spoke of him as much as she did of the others. I was struck by the fact that I had no anticipatory impressions of Uncle Ray. He was my mother's youngest brother, and that was about all I had ever heard of him.

We detoured through Milwaukee and stopped over for a few hours to meet him. It was a Saturday, which was probably just as well. I cannot imagine him challenging the universe by asking a day off from his employers, although he had been working for the same firm for some forty years.

He was a neat, scrubbed, pink-cheeked little man. A bachelor, I was about to say, but the word has acquired sporting overtones; perhaps celibate would be more apt. He had organized our hours in Milwaukee with such precision that one could almost see the utter chaos which threatened to engulf him should he ever step out of the area illuminated by forethought and habit.

He had decided that we should carry away with us some memory of *his* Milwaukee, and as it was nearly lunch time when we arrived he took us to the automat in which he ate his lunch every day. It was vast and efficient, with white-tiled floor, ceiling and walls, excruciatingly hygienic—the perfect antidote to Aunt June, forcing one to admit that although sterility is one answer to brute filth it is not a very good answer. The food was undoubtedly safe and anonymous, and Uncle Ray seemed the epitome of a man who has sustained himself exclusively on such fodder year upon sanitary year. I can recollect nothing from his conversation.

After lunch he hired a cab, which he ordered to tour assorted places at a leisurely pace. He showed us the outside of the anonymous, clean, respectable-looking house wherein he had had his room, and breakfast supplied, over the years. We then drove past a nondescript, square, cream stuccoed, four-storey building which advertised itself as some sort of shipping and warehousing thingummy, and this was where he spent his days working as an accountant. We were then driven along Milwaukee's fashionable lake front and past its half-dozen undistinguished landmarks. I sat in the back seat with Uncle Ray, my mother in the front with the driver. The driver got bored with his patron's dry, precise little lecture on the passing scene and took over himself. Although the travelogue became livelier after that I cannot say that it managed to make Milwaukee irresistible.

After perhaps an hour and a half of this we ended up back at the station. Uncle Ray paid off the cab driver and, after he was safely out of hearing, complained bitterly of having had his thunder stolen. One felt that he had been making the notes for this tour and rehearsing them ever since receiving my mother's letter promising our visit, only to have the cab driver do all the talking. It seemed not unlikely that this was the story of his life.

During these few hours he spent with us he revealed no connections with the world outside his accountancy, his automat feeding (one can scarcely be said to *eat* in an automat, after all), his occupancy of one room in a respectable boarding-house, and his regular Sunday morning attendance at a neat prose Methodist church. His reading was confined to daily papers. He followed no sport, owned no car, dug no garden, listened to no music, appeared to have no intimates. He gave no sign of being happy or unhappy.

Shortly after we visited him he died suddenly of a coronary thrombosis—died even before Uncle Frank, whose death was so visibly on him when we were there. This may well have been the first event in Uncle Ray's life in thirty or forty years—and would have been enough to justify his suspicion that eventfulness was best avoided.

AFTER WE LEFT Milwaukee and headed back towards St Paul-Minneapolis and the Canadian border, ominous signs of the old familiar mother I had known all my life started to appear—the homely intractable mother who weathered storms and outlived contemporaries. The passive euphoria of 'down home' was apparently not for export, but would be confiscated by the Customs officials at the border.

We were bound now for Regina, where we would spend a few days with my sister Florence and her family. So far so good. Nothing prickly in that. Except, as my mother started fussing nearly twenty-four hours in advance, that we should have to travel from Winnipeg to Regina via the Canadian Pacific Railway. She spoke of it rather as if it were The Fate Worse Than Death. She became irritable with me as though it were somehow my fault that we should have to travel C.P.R., and she was prepared to hold me personally responsible for all its sins and omissions.

I eventually got pretty tired of this line of reasoning, and said emphatically that I was tired of it. I pointed out the irrationality of saddling a new, crack transcontinental service with the characteristics of the most obscure branch line (now certainly defunct) of several years back. Almost the entire railway system had been modernized since that historic jaunt of hers. And I refused point-blank to have anything to do with the alternative which she actually suggested, which would have meant travelling Canadian National from Winnipeg to Saskatoon and then changing to another Canadian National train, the chuff-chuff which did the local run from Saskatoon to Regina. It meant an extra train, extra hours of travelling and extra miles. She went on about it though until I got peremptory and said that either the subject was closed or I moved to another and more peaceful coach.

Well, I shouldn't have said that. Not because it was disrespectful—anyone who works hard to earn a little disrespect is entitled to it—but because when we got to Winnipeg the thermometer read 100° Fahrenheit. It was not yet ten o'clock in the morning, and the sky was cloudless.

Our train was in all right, doing the lengthy things trains always do at Winnipeg. We had a leisurely breakfast in the station and then got on and waited for it to depart. And waited. And waited. Train crew and station hands dragged themselves back and forth with a reasonable show of purpose and energy, considering the heat. Massive blocks of ice were being fed into the air-conditioning units. It all looked normal enough, but I *knew*, even before we started. . . . There is a heat above which, and a cold below which, trains just do not keep to schedule. I'm not blaming them; their tolerances of extremes are quite remarkable. At 100° Fahrenheit you're lucky to move, let alone be right on time. That goes for the Canadian National too.

So it came as no surprise really that we were an hour late in pulling out of Winnipeg, and that thenceforward we lost time steadily. About the middle of the afternoon the ice had all melted away, and we were still hours away from Regina. There is nothing more suffocating, more claustrophobic, than an air-conditioned train when the conditioning has gone. There is no way of getting a breath of fresh air or moving air anywhere. All windows and doors are sealed. You realize emphatically that you are trapped—imprisoned. All the babies start to fret and all their mothers to look increasingly harassed. Everyone turns red and boiled looking. The seat covers develop a remarkable and hitherto unsuspected talent for penetrating your clothing, as if they had been made up from surplus hair-shirting. Clothes wilt. Thus it was that soon, on that whole, enormous, immaculate, gleaming, steaming, stainless steel, travel-poster, transcontinental streamliner, there was only one happy person. My mother. The cosmos had graciously justified her every prophecy, her every gripe. She sat bathed in infallibility. The sweat that stung her eyes and turned her clothes sodden she wore like the Victoria Cross. She was so triumphant that she even stopped talking about it—just nonchalantly snapped her watch open now and again to remind me how late the C.P.R. was running.

Finally I mooched off to the club car. I could not, it was true, have a cold beer, but I could have a warm one. It seemed a gallant, defiant gesture. But I had reckoned without Sunday and the Province of Saskatchewan. The Province of Saskatchewan will have no gallant, defiant gestures on a Sunday if they involve beer. Not even warm beer. The law.

We were three, maybe even four, hours late getting into Regina. Who cares? I was sober, and past caring.

We travelled only a little farther together, and that, mercifully, by Canadian National. Back via Saskatoon to Edmonton. I would visit her again before returning to England, but for the time being I was content to deliver her safe and sound to Alice's eldest girl and her husband. They would put her on the train to Regalia the next day, and a couple of hours later Francis would meet her and take her home. In the meantime she settled herself, imperturbable and fulfilled, the classical Chinese portrait of old age as ripeness, with great-grandchildren swooping and darting about her like swallows over a pond.

Bruised and fortified, I went my separate way.